# WITHOUT VISIBLE MEANS OF SUPPORT

This book is dedicated

to

*Doc Slater*

in partial repayment

for

*Eine Kleine Nachtmusik*

played on the pennywhistle.



Printed by Parker & Son, Los Angeles, Calif.

# WITHOUT VISIBLE MEANS OF SUPPORT

by Richard Miller

*The things which are seen*
*are temporal;*
*But the things which are not seen*
*are eternal.*

2 Corinthians IV, 18

PHOTO CREDITS:

Cover—Ben Jansson; 3, 5—Science Museum; 8, Richard duPont Photo Collection; 12—Acme; 15—U.S. Navy; 19, 61, 93, 100, 103—U.S. Army Air Forces; 29, 113—Soaring Society of America; 39, 41—Pathe News; 49, 66—George Uveges; 56—Northrop Aircraft, Inc.; 64—Messerschmitt AG; 80, 86—History Division Los Angeles Co. Museum; 82(t)—Historical Collection, Union Title Insurance Company, San Diego; 82(b)—National Air Museum; 88—Lockheed Missile and Space Co.; 90—University of Santa Clara Archives; 96—Sovfoto; 102—Douglas Aircraft Co.; 104—Air Technical Service Command.

# FOREWORD

BOOKS AND THEIR AUTHORS come to terms in various ways. This one scratched about inside its author for considerably more than a year asking to be let out. In time, and by somewhat roundabout means, it got my attention and made its needs known. After that matters went about as smoothly as they're likely to between authors and their books—or books and their authors.

Although *Without Visible Means of Support* is concerned primarily with the lore of gliding and soaring flight, the reader will find that at times, under the protection of its title, it spills over into the mystical, the occult and the downright spooky. Many readers will undoubtedly feel themselves disinclined to accept this last-mentioned material; and little wonder, for humankind is an audacious lot that has thus far found it possible to disbelieve the Natural Laws of Bacon's *Opus Majus*, the Heliocentricity of Copernicus, the Round Earth of Columbus, the Anatomy of Vesalius, the Evolution of Darwin, the Antisepsis of Semelweiss, the Subconscious Mind of Freud, and a good deal more, with barely a second thought. When, therefore, you arrive at those items which go beyond tickling the outer fringes of inexplicability and leap slap dab into perfect incredibility, you may either leap slap dab after them, or content yourself with the knowledge that they are included in the book at no extra charge, like Green Stamps. *Without Visible Means of Support*, as its title suggests, was not intended for down-to-earth types in any event.

Beyond that, a sincere attempt has been made to assure that the exaggerations in this little volume are as accurate as possible. To keep matters under some degree of control, the book was submitted (prior to publication) to a number of individuals of experience and good taste for their suggestions. Except where they interfered with the narrative, suppressed the excitement, or in any other way changed what I'd written in the first place, these suggestions have been scrupulously heeded. Truth is indeed a marvelous thing, but so valuable (as Mark Twain observed) that we should economize it when we are able.

It has proven, alas, impossible to consult original sources in order to authenticate certain events, names, dates and—when they crop up—facts. This is not due to laziness, nor to the paucity of source material available, but to the author's conviction, already inferred, that most of us are inclined to believe far too little. Thus, when a question of whether or not to include some particularly preposterous or lurid passage has arisen, the decision has inevitably gone in favor of sensationalism.

If, during his passage through this book, the reader should find himself overcome by feelings of outrage and indignation at some of the claims made, he must do his best to choke back his rage. If you find yourself impelled to write a forceful letter stating that the chunk of ice that fell from the sky near Hyperadad, India in 1883 *wasn't* the size of an elephant, or that a lion, an elderly Assyrian priest and a Neanderthal Man were *not* materialized during the séances of Franek Kluski, you are enjoined to check *your* facts closely. We don't want any false accusations without proof.

Go then and sport yourself.

RICHARD MILLER

Santa Monica, California
September, 1967

# CONTENTS

# 1

## Challenge and Response

THE CONTRASTS between soaring flight and powered flight are both numerous and noteworthy. Soaring, for example, is not done despite the weather and the time of day, but because of them; not by schedule, but by impulse. Nor is the soaring pilot at odds with the atmosphere; his progress is *in* it, not *through* it. He makes an aerial excursion, not an incursion. His passage leaves a whisper, not a shriek.

There is also a question of mastery involved, one that points up the manner in which power differs from force. The philosopher Josiah Royce, although he probably knew little about soaring, understood what was at issue. "My son," he stated, "shall learn to sail a boat before he drives a car. In a sailboat he gets power only through his discipline and his ability to meet and master nature. But in the motorcar he gets power without discipline and without control."

Perhaps the point has never been better made than in the statement that, although powered aircraft may express the language of flight, soaring is its eloquence.

## Who Flew First?

IT IS FASCINATING, if not necessarily productive, to trace accounts of early gliding, particularly those in the era B.C. — before Cayley. Cayley is generally regarded as being the first man in modern times — C.1850 — to design and build a flyable glider. He was very far from being the first man to be enchanted by the fact of flight, however, or to attempt to approximate what the birds were doing by some mechanical means or other.

One of the most oft-repeated of early accounts, and one that seems most credible, is that of Danti, a mathematician of Perugia who history records as having made "some faltering glides over Lake Trasimeno about 1490" and who, according to an eye-witness by the name of Crispolti, was seen "with wings fly from a tower across the great Piazza which was densely crowded." During this last flight a structural failure (left wing) resulted in a fall that badly injured the pilot.

Another very early account comes from the Far East. A report given before the Royal Asiatic Society of Bengal in 1938 states that one Abdul Kausim Abbas bin Firnas, who died in 888 A.D., built and flew a successful glider. A reliable historian, according to the account, claimed that Abdul attached two wings to his body and, gaining an eminence, flew a considerable distance. Although he was hurt during the landing of this particular flight, he made later, and better flights.

There is a note in the 1922 edition of *Jane's All the World's Aircraft,* which devotes considerable attention to the then-current developments in gliding, stating that there seemed good reason to believe "that the first experimental gliders were built in a period of remote antiquity." The quote goes on to say that "it has been recorded recently that the natives of certain islands in the Southern Pacific have amused themselves for many generations by gliding from hills into the sea on elementary gliders constructed mainly from palm leaves and a species of cane."

The unfolding of the history of ancient America — America before the influx of Civilization — has brought to light evidence of an extraordinary nature. According to the Polish archaeologist and Hebraic authority M. J. Tenenbaum, the Aztec king Nezahualcoytl utilized a *crir* (Aztec for glider) in descents from the tops of Mexican mountains to the valleys below. Nezahualcoytl was the king of Texcoco, an Aztec city established on the eastern shore of Lake Texcoco toward the end of the 14th century. He was ancient Mexico's most famous poet and philosopher, a patron of the arts and sciences, and himself a notable engineer.

That a man of Nezahualcoytl's accomplishments would have been able to conjure up a glider on his own we need not doubt; still, allowances must be made for the possibility that he was perpetuating a tradition, not inaugurating one. Ancient clay dishes from San Salvador show men flying over palm trees in strange looking machines that may, or may not have existed at a time before, or after Nezahualcoytl. While it is certainly not necessary to accept such slender evidence as proof that gliding took place in very early days, neither is it prudent to dismiss it.

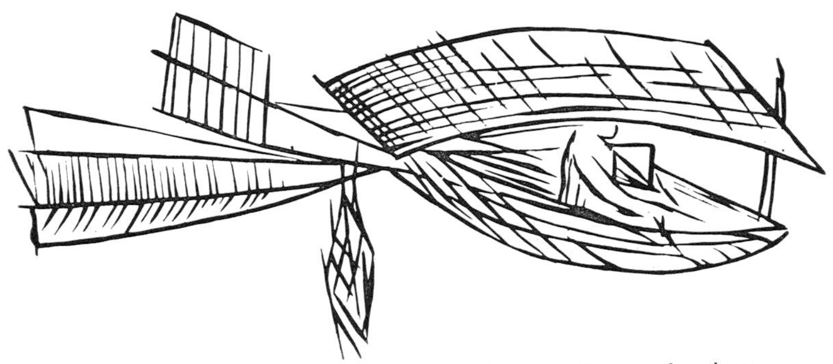

Sketch by Sir George Cayley, executed on the obverse of a silver disc, of a full-scale, man-carrying glider. Date: 1799.

The history of aviation may be so much older than most of us are inclined to believe that flights made 500, or even 1,000 years ago become relatively easy to accept. According to the Akashic readings of the remarkable American clairvoyant Edgar Cayce, the Atlantean civilization, which was terminated by a cataclysm that sank the continent of Atlantis about 10,000 B.C., reached a higher level of scientific achievement than has contemporary civilization.

The Cayce readings assert that the Atlanteans had mastered solar and atomic energy, although probably by more occult means than we employ today, and that they enjoyed radio, television and air travel. Their aircraft seem to have been small carriages with at least a superficial similarity in concept to our air-cushion vehicles, but sustained by some refined method of gravity control. In one Cayce reading, however, reference is made of an escape by air to the Yucatan peninsula in the days just prior to the final catastrophe. It was also revealed that those individuals active in aviation today are the descendants of Atlantis, reincarnated souls in pursuit of lost and forgotten talents.

For the child of the 20th Century the assertion that an ancient civilization, one that flourished 10 or 20,000 years ago and of which no substantial physical remnants are known to exist, surpassed the achievements of modern man will be too wildly improbable to be believed. And yet the Atlanteans finally succeeded in utterly destroying themselves, an accomplishment that modern man has only talked about thus far. Before passing final judgment on Atlantis, therefore, it might be well to wait till all the reports are in.

## Vignettes from The Perilous and Poignant Past (No. 198)

THE TIME WAS the autumn of the year 1929; the place, Chestnut Ridge, a 1200-ft. crest some 40 miles south-southeast of Pittsburgh, Pa., site of the "Allegheny Mountains Soaring Exploration Expedition." The protagonist, and author of the following account, is Wolfgang Klemperer:

"When the *Condor* was again ready [a snagged wingtip had just been repaired] the weather was weak and sultry. Reluctant to trek back up to Bald Knob, we decided to try a more readily accessible launching site on a bare slope on Mr. Nadjent's farm at the 1600-ft. level. The take off by shockcord was easy but lift was insufficient to gain the main ridge. I had to land a couple of miles north of our old airport at the 1200-ft. level before a thunderstorm developed.

"After this we decided not to try any more short cuts but trundled up to our mountain camp and lay in wait for the west wind, listening every hour on our battery powered radio to such weather reports as were being broadcast in those days. Eventually, we got word of the approach of a well developed front and prepared to take it on as it would reach Chestnut Ridge, in hopes to ride it, possibly even to travel with it across the Alleghenies. Everything was in perfect readiness, the barograph wound and sealed by the NAA governor of Virginia as timer, and a fresh shockcord manned by a motley crew of ten strong fellows. On the command "run"—a terrific anticlimax—the tow hook pulled out of the nose of the fuselage. The front moved by. The best chance was missed.

—*Soaring*

## Launch Time

GLIDING AND SOARING are all well and good, but, as generations of pilots have learned, you must get yourself into the air in order to do it—and be more or less prepared to get back on the ground in a systematic and orderly manner if you hope to do it again.

The problem of launching is by no means a simple nor a new one. The most primitive solution to the problem, of course, is simply to use the legs, and as long as gliders were light in weight and limited in maneuverability, legs worked fine. The limitations of this method, however, soon became obvious and the long and colorful search for substitutes began. The history of that search, with its breath-taking triumphs and its footnotes to folly, contributes a particularly rich chapter in the book of human ingenuity.

Sir George Cayley (1773-1857), whose contributions to aviation can hardly be stressed enough, was occupied with the problem of launching from almost the outset of his remarkable career. When he invented the tension (or suspension) wheel in the year 1808 (a device he failed to patent) it was with the intent of providing a light and serviceable undercarriage which would permit a flying machine to gain speed during a take-off run. As the following extract from *Nicholson's Journal* for February, 1810, will show, Cayley was solving a practical, and possibly even pressing problem:

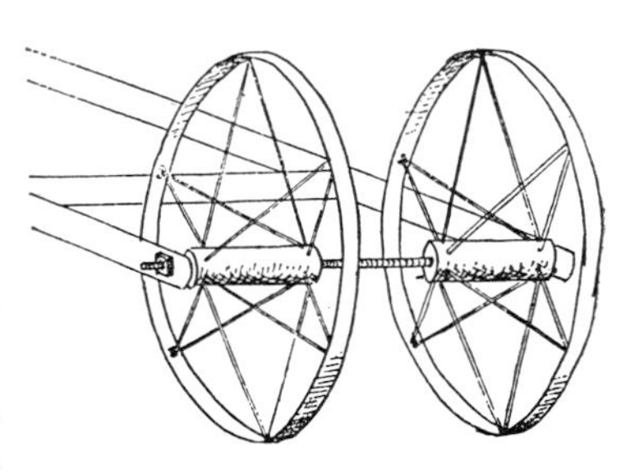

Cayley's design, dating from the year 1808, for a set of tension wheels.

*"Last year I made a machine, having a surface of 300 square feet, which was accidentally broken before there was an opportunity of trying the effect of the propelling apparatus; but its steerage and steadiness were perfectly proved, and it would sail obliquely downward in any direction, according to the set of the rudder. Even in this state, when any person ran forward with it, with his full speed, taking advantage of a gentle breeze in front, it would bear upward so strongly as scarcely to allow him to touch the ground; and would frequently lift him up, and convey him several yards together."*

Cayley was too progressive a thinker to depend long on such a rudimentary method of launching. In what appears to have been his next successful glider, the "Old Flyer" of 1849, he has advanced to the use of a tricycle landing gear and outside help for getting airborne. This machine, bearing a 10-year-old boy, "was floated off the ground for several yards on descending a hill, and also for about the same space by some persons pulling the apparatus against a very slight breeze by a rope." Let it be noted that Cayley anticipated later experimenters with his very specific suggestions for the use of an artificial hill (Lilienthal), a swinging rope (Le Bris) and a balloon (Montgomery) as launching appointments. But, by the provisions of that perverse law that rewards men in inverse proportion to the quality of their accomplishments, Cayley was quickly forgotten and his methods subsequently rediscovered by other experimenters of similar, if not quite equal genius.

The simplest alternative method of getting a glider into the air, once the pilot's feet have been given the job of pushing the rudder pedals, is simply to pick the thing up and throw it. It's not quite that simple, however, for a workable launch depends on the proper combination of glider, slope and throwing technique. Hand launching, nonetheless, has been successfully used on many occasions and was a means employed frequently by the Wrights.

Ground-based apparatus (other than winches) has a history of sorts, but has tended to give way to more flexible methods as they were developed. The problem with building a launching way, or laying a set of tracks was that the wind was likely to blow in some way other than the way the way builder or the track layer had in mind. Lilienthal's artificial hill, which was built for his use near Lichterfield in 1894, got around the wind problem by being conical, thus facing all directions at once. A number of other gliding hills were built subsequent to Lilienthal's example by various groups including one by Messrs. Handley Page on their flying grounds at Cheekmouth, between Dagenham and Barking, England, in the year 1909. In the main, however, it has proven more economical to take the glider to the hill rather than bringing the hill to the glider and we are hard pressed to cite any recent examples in this category.

When, *faut de mieux,* a set of tracks were laid out for glider launching they were generally on a slope so gentle that some external source of power was necessary in order to get the machine up to flying speed. Gravity acting on a weight attached to a cable, connected via a system of pulleys either directly to the glider, or to a launching trolley, was used on more than one occasion. The Wrights hoisted their weight to the top of a small tower prior to launching. A quarter century later another experimenter, employing the same principle, realized that he could do the necessary weight lifting *after* the launch—providing he survived—by dropping the ballast into a well hole. The decline of the Protestant Ethic, still a viable doctrine in the heyday of the Wrights, and the emergence of the Fly-Now, Pay-Later Attitude, so pervasive today, is surprisingly apparent in these two instances. Complete moral collapse is evident at a still later date (1944) in the example of a group of British POW's who, having built an escape glider in the attic of the castle in which they were incarcerated, devised a launching scheme which involved dropping a huge conglomeration of iron and stone into the courtyard below with complete disregard for the safety of their captors and no thought of *ever* retrieving the weight.

Perhaps the rarest of all glider launching apparatus is the inclined slipway. The most notable, if not the only example of such a launching way is the one Jose Weiss erected on Bury Hill, a location about half a mile north of the Whiteways in Sussex, England. It was a structure of light steel trusses which provided a run of about 45 feet and an incline of roughly 20 degrees. A ballast-and-pulley system, contained within the structure, provided additional launching power.

LONE
EAGLE

By the time he built his launchway, probably 1908, Weiss was far too seasoned an experimenter to be outdone by the wind. Accordingly, he mounted the entire structure on a central pivot which was also the center of a circular rail that bore, through the agency of four rollers on the lowermost members, the weight of the way. Thus it could be pivoted to face a wind from any direction.

The slipway seems to have been Weiss's solution to the problem of launching some of his heavier (up to 40 kgs.) models; it seems doubtful that it was ever used for the larger, man-carrying machines. These were operated from Mount Amberley, a small hill near Arundel, also in Sussex. Here a glider would be perched on the crest of the hill where a good push, at the precise moment, would launch the machine over the brink and into the ascending currents. It was with a start such as this that Eric Gordon England made a soaring flight with a 40-ft. gain of height on June 27th, 1909.

The endeavors of yet one more early pioneer, Cayley's contemporary, Jean-Marie Le Bris, are necessary in order to amplify our appreciation of the problems which faced those resourceful men who had to solve all the problems, from first to last, by their own means. Le Bris was a French sea captain who, by his fortieth year (1856), had retired from sailing and built his first glider. This machine, in which the pilot stood upright, was apparently launched successfully on a beach near Douarnenez a Trefeuntec by kiting it off the bed of a cart or carriage drawn against the wind by a horse. The surviving account of this episode holds that Le Bris attained an altitude in excess of 300 feet and that he landed with no further incident than a groundloop.

At a later date Le Bris attempted another type of launch. Unlike his use of the horse, which provided some lively times for those who followed that lead, his new method never seems to have had great appeal. It comprised suspending the glider on a rope beneath a sort of scaffold in such a manner that it could be

Cloyd Artman enjoyed a brief, meteoric career as a glider builder and soaring pilot in the Pacific Northwest in the early 1930's. After designing and building his own glider, and teaching himself to fly, Artman solved the launch problem by this daring method.

oscillated and released—Cayley's idea put into practice! The scaffold, being of limited height, was built adjacent to a quarry. Height and depth figures given for the set-up vary from one account to the next, but we might accept 30 feet for the height of the one and 70 feet for the depth of the other from among the choices—and grant a large measure of courage to Le Bris.

It seems apparent that the pilot grossly underestimated the speed necessary for flight and that following his release the issue in balance was whether airspeed or the bottom of the quarry would come up first. As ill luck would have it, the airspeed lost, the glider was demolished, and Le Bris was unable to climb out of the quarry due to the fact that one of his legs was broken and generally he wasn't feeling too well. The crash in the quarry was effectively the end of his active flying career. His finances never again permitted him the luxury of flight.

* * *

MORE GLIDER LAUNCHES have probably been made by winch—millions and millions of them—than by any other means. Although it doesn't offer quite the flexibility that a towplane does, a winch is more economical to operate and offers an excellent means of contacting lift when it exists. The modern winch, with its fluid-drive transmission, tensionometer, safety enclosure and guillotine is a highly efficient piece of equipment, and one with a long history.

One of the earliest instances of winch launching occurred at the St. Louis World Fair in 1904. The pilot was William Avery, one of Chanute's associates from the Indiana sand dune days (C. 1898), who probably flew a Chanute glider or something very close to it. Although it is assumed that the winch in question was powered by an internal-combustion engine, the point is not certain. There is a still earlier report, impossible to verify, of a powered apparatus with drum and cable, but that was in another land. And besides, the winch is dead.

The earliest winch of all, so far as the available records go, was a hand-driven affair employing 400 meters of fishing line devised by Percy Pilcher. To Pilcher must also go the credit for improvising the first pulley tow. His system was powered by a horse and provided a mechanical advantage at the glider end of the rope.

If there is one tendency apparent throughout the history of the development of glider launching methods, the aim of which tendency is a self-contained system, it is the quest for independence. This was something the hang glider pilots enjoyed as a consequence of their light-weight machines and leg-assisted take off, something which was lost as gliders became heavier and more complex, and something which the glider pilot has sought to regain ever since. The desire for self-sufficiency, whether a matter of necessity or a trait of character—a fair enough assumption in the case of soaring pilots—has resulted in more than one odd undertaking.

The case of Mr. John Dolza of Fenton, Michigan, was clearly a matter of necessity. Some years ago Mr. Dolza found himself with a glider, an airport to launch it from, and plenty of sky to fly it in, but no means of getting it airborne. Mr. Dolza's solution to the problem was to build himself a radio-controlled winch that could be operated entirely from the cockpit of the sailplane by the pilot during the launch. Mr. Dolza was keenly aware of such hazards as having the empty glider dragged down the field and shredded through the winch, so incorporated a number of appropriate safeguards in his six-channel system.

While, by his own admission, Mr. Dolza's motivation for building his unique winch came from his inability to find any fellow gliding enthusiasts, let alone reliable winch operators, that of Mr. John Fisher, of Australia, seems to have resulted from his inability to find *anybody*. Of course if Mr. Fisher hadn't been a somewhat self-contained individual himself he wouldn't have been living alone in a caravan on the top of a mountain at the end of the world with a Schneider *Kingfisher,* a glider he'd built himself, as his principal companion.

Mr. Fisher's hill was Mt. Elliot, 3071 feet above sea level in the Australian Alps of New South Wales. His perch was at a point some nine rough miles from the town of Carryong and accessible to four-wheel drive vehicles. To a man of Mr. Fisher's temperament the problem of staking out his 100 feet of cable and bungy, fashioning a ground-anchor to secure the tail prior to take off, and releasing himself by a line running from the cockpit, provided no challenges he was unable to meet and master. When the method proved to be successful it was used for

Self-contained launching systems have been the dream of soaring pilots for generations. This one, devised by Dick Devine and tested at Palos Verdes Hills near Redondo, California, about 1931 is said to have provided a launch speed of nearly 100 m.p.h.

many subsequent flights. Most of these terminated on the flats 2000 feet below launch height, from which point, as might be expected of him, Mr. Fisher effected his own retrieves.

* * *

LAUNCHING FROM THE GROUND, no matter how well done, has limitations that only a more direct means, such as employing another aircraft, can overcome. However, because aerial launching always involves two flying machines, and generally two aeronauts, it tends to be more complex, more demanding, and inherently more dramatic. What the complexities and demands were on the morning of March 16, 1905, when Daniel Maloney was hoisted 800 or so feet above the California countryside in a Montgomery tandem monoplane glider, borne aloft by a hot-air balloon, we can readily imagine. That there was drama appropriate to the adventure we can scarcely doubt.

Daniel Maloney seems to have had somewhat the same attitude toward the glider that Lincoln Beachey did toward the airplane. He was an Irishman, apparently quite fearless, and one of a number of pilots employed to test and exhibit the Montgomery machines. He made many more flights following the success of the attempt on March 16th, the best recorded instance being an exhibition flight made from the campus of the University of Santa Clara, in northern California, on the afternoon of April 29th, 1905. It is stated that on this occasion he was lifted to an altitude of 4,000 feet beneath a hot-air balloon, released, and, on his way down in the 43-lb. glider, did "startling turns, spirals, figure eights, hair-raising dives and other difficult evolutions . . . with ease and grace." More of that story presently.

It was great fun while it lasted, evidently, but, as in Beachey's case, it didn't last very long. Maloney was killed on July 18th, 1905. He was the third pilot, following Lilienthal and Pilcher, to die in the crash of a glider.

Few people seemed eager to follow Maloney's example. This is hardly surprising in light of the complexity and expense of balloon launching, not to mention the hazards. These are amply demonstrated in the account of an attempt made by Wolfgang Klemperer in 1922 at Duebendorf Airport, Zurich, Switzerland. Klemperer and a number of other glider pilots were on hand with their gliders to take part in an air show sponsored by the Swiss. Apparently no one had foreseen the necessity of launching the gliders, and no provisions to do so had been made.

After some theorizing by Klemperer, and some preparation to the *Blue Mouse,* which had been shipped from Aachen for the exhibition, a practice launch was attempted. This was on the day before the air show was to begin, using one of the captive gas balloons of the Swiss Air Service. As it chanced the length of the attach cable, plus the mass of the glider, proved an excellent combination for inducing a slow, but uncontrollable oscillation between the balloon and the *Blue Mouse.* Klemperer realized that he would need all the altitude he could get if he was to release successfully. He shouted to the winch operator, asking to be taken higher. The operator, misunderstanding his command, began reeling in cable instead of letting out more.

At this point Klemperer felt impelled to release. The glider immediately entered a flat spin which no combination of control movements could counteract. There was nothing to do but wait for the inevitable crash, an event which very shortly took place immediately in front of the empty grandstands. Klemperer was thrown out of the cockpit, *sans* shoes, onto the grass, but was not seriously hurt.

Although Klemperer was unquestionably chastened by his misadventure in Switzerland he was by no means at the end of his tether. The passage of a few years was to see him again involved in a launch using a lighter-than-air vehicle. This new exploit occurred in the fall of the year 1929, at which time Klemperer was living in America and employed, as Manager of Research, by the Goodyear-Zeppelin Corporation of Akron, Ohio.

There were many similarities between the tow from Akron and the episode seven years earlier in Zurich. Once again an air show was the occasion, once again the means at hand were unproven, and once again the venture fell short of total success. The air show was the 1929 Cleveland Air Races, to which, it was proposed, Klemperer should tow in his new sailplane, the *Akron Condor*. The tow ship provided was the Goodyear pony blimp, *Vigilant*.

The take off and initial part of the flight went well enough, but as progress was made the air became more turbulent and it became increasingly difficult to hold station behind the airship. Finally the glider, which had neither airbrakes nor spoilers, drew abreast of the bobbing *Vigilant* and the towing cable detached itself. Klemperer soared along in the vicinity of the blimp for a spell, and even contemplated making an attempt to catch the dangling cable in his hand at one point, but judged that it was whipping about too violently to permit safe retrieval. Presently a safe landing was made at Babb's fruit farm near North Royalton, Ohio. Here a crack was discovered in the fuselage skin which made it wise to abandon any further attempt to get to Cleveland.

Slightly less than five months after Klemperer's landing near North Royalton, on January 31, 1930, Capt. Ralph S.

Barnaby, U.S.N., checked out the rigid airship *Los Angeles,* then docked at the Lakehurst (N.J.) Naval Air Station, hooked up his Prufling, and went for a little hop. It was a little more complicated than that, of course, requiring some assistance from the airship crew and the cooperation of an admiral or two, but these were details of secondary importance in the event. Barnaby remained in the control cabin of the *Los Angeles* during the ascent and only climbed into the glider when the airship reached an altitude of 3,000 feet. The 13-min. ride that followed release was uneventful except for a little soaring that Barnaby was able to do at 200 feet over one of the dirigible hangars.

(This was not the first nor the last time that a glider was carried by a rigid airship, but apparently the first time a drop was made. As early as 1918 the Germans put biplane wings on a torpedo, making a glider of it. It was carried, along with an Albatross D.3 beneath the L-35. In later years a *President* was carried aloft by the LZ-127, and at one time the *Graf Zeppelin* carried a sailplane.)

In the understandably brief annals of lighter-than-air glider towing, only a bit of fantasy remains. Richard C. duPont, who was unquestionably aware of the unique stratospheric tows made by the Russians in 1936 (see TOWS TO THE STRATOSPHERE), contemplated using a balloon to launch him from an altitude of 60,000 to 70,000 ft. from whence, as one account described it, "he may glide to either coast, a distance of 1,500 miles." Quite aside from the 100-plus glide ratio involved, a venture of this sort would require a pressurized cockpit (or pressure suit) and a sailplane of very special construction. In the more than thirty years since duPont's proposal, no such sailplane has been built, although one is currently (1967) under construction in the U.S.

* * *

WHEN IT WAS REALIZED, beginning about 1930, that it was possible to soar over flat land as well as over hilly terrain, and as ever greater freedom from bungy launching was sought, the airplane grew accordingly in popularity as a towing vehicle. Following the initial use of the method just after World War I (see TONY FOKKER AND THE FIRST AERO TOWS), and its reintroduction by Espenlaub, Raab and Katzmeier in 1927, the technique was enthusiastically exploited by the Russians who launched a series of long-distance air trains.

Thousands and thousands of tow planes have come and gone since the air train days. The apparent willingness of the glider pilot to hook his sailplane to anything headed up has resulted in a vast variety of apparatus, some modified, some improvised and some, like the He.111Z (two fuselage, five engines), built specially for the purpose. The most recent innovation in glider towing, the helicopter, was introduced by the Poles in 1957 and used for aerial retrieving (the only kind permitted) during the World Championships at Junin, Argentina, in 1963.

Not even a helicopter, however, could offer the sort of ride Paul Bikle once had behind a P-51. The flight was made in March, 1952, from El Mirage Field near Adelanto, California, for the avowed purpose of checking the oxygen system in Bikle's then-new Schweizer 1-23E. To keep the tow speed down to 120 m.p.h. the P-51, piloted by Air Force Captain Dick Johnson—not the soaring Dick Johnson—was flown with flaps and gear fully extended. The tow rope was tied around the tail wheel casting of the 51.

The plan was to tow to 30,000 feet, but eight minutes after take off, at an altitude of 17,000 feet, Johnson, who was dressed only in a light summer flying suit, had enough of the icy blasts streaming into the cockpit from the open landing gear doors and waved the glider off. If this extraordinary tow fell somewhat short of expectations, neither of the extraordinary participants did. Dick Johnson went on to become Chief of Flight Testing at General Dynamics and Bikle, his oxygen system working faultlessly, ultimately established a world absolute altitude record of 46,267 ft. in the 1-23.

## A Look Into the Seeds of Time

MICHEL de NOTREDAME was born in St. Remy (Provence) in 1503 and died (of arthritic gout) a little before sunrise on the morning of July 2, 1566, precisely the time he had predicted for his passing. Nostradamus, as he is known to our epoch, was the greatest Western prophet since Biblical times. He left many volumes of quatrains containing predictions regarding the future history of the world, and world history has unfolded since with remarkably little deviation from these prophecies.

We shall concern ourselves with a single quatrain here, number 57 from Century V, which gives, in its first line, specific reference to the name Montgolfier, that of the brothers of Annonay who first successfully flew a hot-air balloon on June 5, 1783, substantially 200 years after Nostradamus mentioned the event. The second line of the quatrain (*Qui par le trou advertira l'armée*) gives reference to the first military use of the new invention which occurred on June 16, 1794. In this instance, at the Battle of Fleurus, observer Captain J.M.J. Coutelle "at the hole" (*par le trou*) reconnoitered the Austrian positions and informed the French of their deployment (*advertira l'armée*).

The final lines of the quatrain seem to refer to the Treaty of Tolentino and the serious decline in the fortunes of Pius VI. The date of the treaty was February 19, 1797. By its terms the Pope lost Avignon, Venaissin, Bolognia, Ferrara and Romagnia. Little matter, for shortly after this he was taken out of Italy, to Valence, where he shortly died, this being told in Quatrain 46 of Century VIII—and that a good long while before the event.

## Vignettes from The Perilous and Poignant Past (No. 27)

THE TIME WAS toward the close of World War II; the event, a glider landing in enemy-held territory. The protagonist is Robert Somerscales, a British pilot whose duty is to get his fully loaded *Horsa,* an 88-ft. troop glider, on the ground with the least possible damage to the men and materiel aboard:

"Dark puffs kept appearing in the sky around us. Just beyond the beaches we released, and the normal pandemonium of a mass landing commenced. Unorthodox flying was normal and normal flying was non-existent. A Dakota tug in front with one engine blazing was dropping the supplies prematurely, and the gaily colored parachutes were drifting across the approach path and threatening to become effective cockpit covers to the blunt noses of the weaving Horsas.

"The glider defenses on the L.Z. had obviously not been cleared as expected and it appeared that the Hamilcar zone some distance away had received preference, as the huge gliders were already disgorging their tanks into action unimpeded.

"The real nature of these defences now became clear. Telegraph poles about 30 feet high were planted with German precision at intervals of less than a wingspan in a neat and orderly pattern of squares and cross-braced with steel wire in all directions at the uppermost ends. Well, thank goodness it had not been in their nature to plant the poles at random. The whole effect was rather like a gigantic hop field. The 'lanes' of the poles were near enough into the wind thank goodness.

"With only seconds now before the inevitable landing nasty thoughts raced through my mind. Those wires! Too fast and too low and chances of decapitation round about the neck were high. Too high and too slow and a stall on top of a wire may well decapitate one longitudinally as it were. With speed and height just right perhaps we should get away with it.

"At a hundred feet and 80 knots on the clock we pulled out of our 75-degree approach angle and slowly lost height and speed until we were just clearing the wires, and at what I judged to be the right moment I dropped the nosewheel into the wire. The effect was immediate and quite helpful, almost as good as a deck arrester. As we rapidly lost flying speed the wingtips were

neatly removed by impact with the poles, and the glider came to rest in a cloud of dust.

"The sounds of flight now gave way to the sounds of mortar bombs exploding and small-arms fire. Incendiaries were making sickening patterns across the landing zone and some gliders were in flames. There was an urgency to get out. We felt slightly safer prone under the glider and adding a little to the weight of our small-arms fire. Occasionally we could hear frantic movement in the fuselage section and seconds later the rear fuselage and tail fell away with a crash. Chains were released and Jeep and Six-Pounder emerged with its crew of eight Ox and Bucks Light Infantry more happy than I had seen them since take off. They were now in *their* element. We waved as they screamed off to their rendezvous in low gear and suddenly we realized that many months of training had paid off.

"The area was no longer healthy and we moved off at the double in the direction of our rendezvous but paused in the shelter of a ditch to look back. Our *Horsa* was proudly showing its invasion stripes to the sky and not yet burning.

"Don said quietly: 'Well, that's one we shan't have to bloody well retrieve.' "

—*Sailplane and Gliding*

## Soaring Over the Sea

CONVECTION OVER THE SEA, because of the relatively more homogeneous surface of water areas, tends to be more regular than over land. It may be considered to occur in a more representative or primordial form, that of a series of alternating clockwise and counterclockwise rolls on up-and-downwind axes. The same pattern, although it may tend to form over land, is broken up and distorted by the many discontinuities common to land areas.

The relatively regular pattern of maritime convection has given rise to many hopes of long soaring flights over water. The long, regular rolls seem, at first glance, to offer an excellent means of soaring for long distances without circling. This theoretical advantage is offset by the fact that ocean convection, due to the small temperature differential between the surface water and the surrounding air, does not tend to go very high as a rule. Picking a landing spot, of course, is not a problem, but the retrieve is probably the sort of thing that only exceptionally strong swimmers would want to try.

To date, largely for the evident reason—and despite the fact that many many seaplane gliders have been successfully built and flown—there have been no real serious attempts to soar over the ocean; all the glory that goes with new achievements still awaits the pioneers. Nevertheless, some quite notable over-water flights have been made.

The first over-water flights of any consequence came about as the result of a competition for the first double crossing of the English Channel, in a sailplane, sponsored by the London *Daily Mail* and backed up by a cash prize of £1000. On the first day of the competition, June 20th, 1931, Robert Kronfeld, in his *Wien*, aero-towed to 10,000 ft. from St. Inglevert, France, and—there being no stipulations regarding soaring—simply glided to Dover. Then he took another tow and glided back to St. Inglevert. An English pound was worth close to five dollars in those days; at roughly $2500 a crossing these were probably the highest priced glider flights ever made.

A soaring flight across the Channel, of course, was a far more sporting proposition and a prospect that enticed many a

British pilot. It is recorded that, in 1932, the year after Kronfeld's glides in the *Wien,* Mr. P. Michelson kept his *Cloudcraft Phantom* at Dover where he hoped one day to gain sufficient altitude by slope soaring to glide to the French coast with a following wind. No immortality for Michelson and the *Cloudcraft Phantom,* however; nor for Philip Wills and *Hjordis*—not on August 15th, 1937, at least—who soared together from Dunstable to Dover, arrived at the coast with 4,000 ft. of altitude, but failed to gain enough additional height to make the attempt practicable.

At the British national contest, Dunstable, July 1938, a special prize was offered for crossing the channel. On the 13th Kit Nicholson got as far as Lympne, near the coastal town of Folkestone, but found the air unenthusiastic. It was still unenthusiastic when Philip Wills got there, now flying a *Minimoa,* on the 4th of September. The time had not yet come.

Perhaps all that was necessary was to have something other than a cross-Channel flight scheduled, as G. H. Stephenson did on April 22nd, 1939, when he took a winch tow at Dunstable and set off toward Reigate, a town about 15 miles south of London, where he was to attend an engagement party for the lady who is today Ann Welch. It was a better day for soaring than for an engagement party, so Stephenson, flying a *Kirby Gull,* proceeded on to the coast, which he crossed between Dover and Folkestone, and across the Channel. The 24 miles flown over water passed without incident and Stephenson landed the *Gull* at le Wast, near Boulogne, less than three hours after his start from Dunstable. The total flight was 127 miles, quite creditable even without considering its pioneering nature.

With the ice broken cross-Channel flights became increasingly popular. For a while, with the higher performance sailplanes, they became easier too. As of 1961, eleven pilots had made the crossing, one, Lorne Welch, twice. Today, because of airspace restrictions, however, such a flight is almost impossible.

* * *

As IN ALL THINGS, necessity is also a prime determinant in over-water soaring. With this in mind we should be quite prepared to learn that the Scandinavian soaring pilots are probably responsible for more such flights than any other group. The first crossing of note in the Nordic countries was one from Denmark to Sweden, a total distance of some 15 miles, made on June 6th, 1936. As in the case of the first Channel crossings the pilot was a German (Peter Riedel) and there was a prize involved, although Peter was unaware of it at the time he made the flight. In the years since World War II over-water flights in Scandinavia have become increasingly common, and the distances longer.

Although many flights involving water crossings have been made in Scandinavia, clearly none was more daring, nor more exciting, than the one made in an *Olympia* across the northern part of the Kattegat, the sea that separates Denmark and Sweden, by the Dane, Dyhr Thomsen, in 1956. The distance of this particular crossing, landfall to landfall, is approximately 45 miles. The duration of that part of the flight spent over water was one and a half hours!

Thomsen's adventure began near Herning, in middle Denmark, and progressed in a northeasterly direction for about 100 miles. This brought him to the east coast of Denmark at a point near its northern tip. About a third of the way across the stretch of water that now separated him from Sweden, Thomsen could see the island of Laeso, his stepping stone to the other side. He had anticipated the water crossing from the start and had hoped for a cu-nim to do for him what the parting of the waters had done for Moses. The flight out of Egypt had better luck; Thomsen's first thermal at the coast wasn't even adequate to give him the height he needed to start the crossing and there was nothing resembling a cu-nim in sight.

When he made his second, and successful start further to the north Thomsen was in a less favorable position, now being fated to cross to the north of Laeso rather than directly over it. This notwithstanding he left the coast in his get-away thermal at an altitude of somewhat over 3,000 ft., climbed to almost 4,000 ft., then settled back to around the 3,200-ft. level. A half an hour drifting with the wind brought the *Olympia* to a point just north of Laeso. The difficult two-thirds of the flight now remained to be done.

Laeso is a sizeable island. It has an airfield and is large enough to be the source of some thermal activity. In the event it had produced a fair-sized cumulus which, at the time of Thomsen's arrival, was on its own, drifting toward Sweden, some distance to the northeast of the island. All well and good, except that attempting to intercept the cloud would mean abandoning the island for good. One other possibility (other than landing in the water) presented itself; nearby was a ship carrying a load of lumber, a miniature aircraft carrier made to order!

The decision, of course, was to go for the cloud. By the time Thomsen reached its lift he was down to 2.500 ft., his lowest point during the crossing — and pretty low! The contact was successful, however, and the thermal proved quite serviceable, providing a climb to 4,500 ft. and a tremendous feeling of relief. Thomsen stayed snug in his friendly little cumulus for quite a while before looking out again. The security he felt in his altitude blind, however, began to give way to his anxiety about the constancy of the wind. Finally the desire to see land became quite urgent, so he straightened out on a compass course for Sweden.

When Thomsen emerged from the cloud he could see the coast he so coveted in the distance. At this point he calculated a 44:1 glide-to-land angle for the *Olympia* and, satisfied with the figures, set out for the shore at 44 m.p.h. He flew on to the coast without further incident, but arrived over land with too little altitude to catch the thermal that would have permitted him to continue on to Stockholm, his goal. Thus the flight ended at Kungsbacka, a town a few miles inland from the Kattegat, at two o'clock in the afternoon.

# 2

## Audio Aids to Instrumentation

A SOUND of a given pitch, tone or volume is an excellent means of conveying information, as anyone who has ever owned a dog will readily testify. A sound, provided it's in the correct range, makes itself heard. The data it contains can, as a rule, be assimilated and acted upon with less conscious evaluation and interpretation than, say, information conveyed visually. The audio attachment to the variometer provides an excellent example of the advantages inherent in the use of sound to transmit information of consequence to the soaring pilot.

For a good long time before the audio attachment became commonplace, soaring pilots were in the habit of adjusting or maintaining airspeed by the sound of the passing airstream. The deliberate use of sound as a flying aid did not begin with the whining Crossfell, however. Gliding lore offers us the story of one Herman Lindner who, it is stated, tuned the flying wires of the University of Illinois' Waco primary to play *Never My God to Thee* when the ship approached placard speed.

Then there was Mungo Buxton's *Scud*. The *Scud* was a small single-place glider not unpopular in England prior to World War II, one example of which was still flying at last report. Buxton's was fitted with a network of fine copper tubes which opened at their outer ends flush with the surfaces of the wing. The internal ends all met in a sort of miniature telephone exchange located on the *Scud's* panel. By means of a stethoscope plugged into this nexus the pilot could monitor airflow over the wing and thereby predict stalling speed with considerable accuracy.

In the early 1930's Captain Ralph S. Barnaby, whose glider drop from beneath the *Los Angeles* is covered elsewhere (see LAUNCH TIME), experimented with an aural blind-flying system. At the time Barnaby was stationed at the Pensacola, Florida, Naval Air Station and owned a Franklin PS-2 utility glider which he used as a test bed for his trials.

The inspiration for his experiments came in part from Barnaby's fascination with the effects one experiences when placed between two speakers broadcasting the same transmission. The sound seems to originate either to the right or left, depending on which broadcast is nearer. When equally spaced between the two sources one has the impression that the sound is originating in his head. From this Barnaby reasoned that if a noise-maker with a volume roughly proportional to the velocity of the air actuating it could be mounted on each wing tip, and the sound piped to the corresponding ear, that the pilot, by keeping the sound centered, could maintain a straight course during blind flight. This satisfied the theoretical demands of the directional-control mode of operation.

Because of its simplicity the part of the system connected with airspeed control was the first to be tried. Barnaby began by testing a variety of 5-and-10-cent store horns and whistles. At length he found two horns with relatively little lag or hysteresis and in which the volume of sound, once the metal reeds began to vibrate, was practically independent of speed. One of these sounded off at 25, the other at 30 m.p.h., speeds that nicely bracketed the 27 m.p.h. cruising speed of the Franklin.

The 25 and 30-m.p.h. horns were taped side by side to the right front wing strut of the glider a few feet out from the fuselage and flight tests were started. At speeds in excess of 30 m.p.h., a roaring pace in those days, the pilot would hear a chord, the result of both horns blowing. If only a single note sounded the glider's speed was in the normal cruising range. If the noise stopped altogether—stall occurred at about 23 m.p.h.—it was past time to push the stick forward. "When the horns stopped singing," an acquaintance of Barnaby's quipped, "the angels started."

For his directional-control system Barnaby needed a pair of sound generators whose noise was proportional to airspeed. This requirement was met by two rotary mechanisms, also obtained from the 5-and-10-cent store, which were mounted one to a wing tip and connected to lengths of aluminum tubing that transmitted the sound to the cockpit. As in the case of Mungo Buxton's *Scud,* the sounds were monitored with a stethoscope, this one obtained from the station dispensary.

When everything was ready Barnaby tested his aural blind-flying system by gliding for brief periods with his eyes shut. From a mechanical point of view everything worked fine; the weak link in the chain, the inventor confessed, was the inventor. The sounds would come through the stethoscope indefinitely, or at least as long as the glider kept flying, but the longest Barnaby could force himself to keep his eyes closed was 30 seconds.

* * *

It is difficult to think of noise, for some reason, without thinking of Texas. As everyone knows, or should know, Texas generally provides its own unique solutions to its own unique problems. As everyone also knows, or should know, variometer readings are obtained as a consequence of air flowing into or out of a reservoir through an orifice. It follows, of course, that the larger the reservoir and the larger the orifice, the greater potential precision of the instrument. It should further be obvious that the entire glider is an air reservoir of sorts, and that could all the airflow into and out of *it* be channeled through a single opening, there would be no need to carry a separate air container to power the variometer.

Sealing a sailplane, however, would be a costly and complex job and one that would require either sealing the pilot in or sealing him out, both poor alternatives. Besides, all pilots are equipped with a self-sealing air reservoir, with auxiliary audio device, in the form of the human respiratory system. As a rule the capacity of the lungs is not great (we're getting back to the Lone Star State by stages), but the rate of air flow, on which the variometer depends for successful operation, is a function of two factors, capacity and rate of vertical displacement—climb or descent. If the rate of climb were great enough, therefore, the air contained in an aspirin bottle would be adequate to give a reading.

Thus, insomuch as everybody knows, or should know, that rate of climb depends on thermal strength, which in turn depends on hot air, we finally get back to the Sovereign State of Texas; where, as everybody knows, the thermals are very strong and the human respiratory system, complete with auxiliary audio device, developed to a point seldom encountered elsewhere. And so it is, insomuch as this entire business must eventually reach some sort of conclusion, that we find the Texan putting his thermals to the test by the simple expedient of puckering up his lips. If he hears himself whistle, he sticks with it; if not, he looks elsewhere.

## Vignettes from The Perilous and Poignant Past (No. 51)

THE TIME WAS the Nineteen Thirties; the place, Midwestern U.S.A. The protangonist is Ed Heath, the author anonymous:

"He motioned us to stand clear, gave Lambert a pre-arranged signal. The motor of the *Standard* commenced its roving song and the big ship 500 feet away moved off with the Heath *Super Soarer* in tow. Before it had travelled 100 feet the glider was skimming along about five feet high, and Ed was flying it as fast as possible to cut down resistance and allow the *Standard* to get up flying speed. After the *Standard* had gained a little altitude Ed nosed up a little and the way the glider soared up to about 100 feet above the tow plane was so sudden and thrilling to see that an exclamation of pleased excitement burst from the little crowd around me.

". . . Suddenly close observers saw the *Standard* gain rapidly on the glider which seemed to be trying to point its nose at the zenith, then, while in this position the tail was blown upon by the following breeze, and as the tail had little inertia, and great leverage on the rest of the ship, it moved in a quarter circle until the ship was on its back, from which position Ed dived it right into three more loops just like the first. After this thrilling exhibition we could hear Ed's voice which was one of the most penetrating in the aviation world (I have heard him explain things to students from almost 1,000 feet up) telling us to stand back so he could land where he started from, which he almost did, but this was no surprise as he often won spot landing competitions at air meets in a Heath *Parasol*.

"Ed says that when released from the tow plane the glider drops from 60 back to 25 m.p.h. so suddenly that one must take care not to bump his head against the instrument board, and if loops are to be made, they must be made right away before the extra speed is lost, or the glider will stall hopelessly before it even points straight up, and a loop will be impossible. He also states that a glider loop has to be made from a down wind start, as the wind is relied upon to blow the tail around. Diving for speed does not help, for the glider is so lightly loaded and has so much resistance that it dives but little better than a parachute . . ."

—*The 1932 Flying and Glider Manual*

## Tony Fokker and the First Aero Tows

ANTONY FOKKER, like Willy Messerschmitt, Frederick Handley Page, Henri Farman, Victor Ilyushin, Glenn Curtiss, Charles Lindbergh and many another noted aviation pioneer, took a fling at gliding at one point in his very remarkable career. His participation in the first British soaring contest at Itford Hill, Sussex, in the fall of 1922 produced results typical of Fokker. He took two gliders to England with him, made the first two-place soaring flight on record (during which the first motion pictures from a glider in flight were taken), and at one point, by virtue of remaining aloft for 37 min., was chief contender for the prize of £1000 that the *Daily Mail* offered for the longest flight of the meet. It seems quite likely that Fokker could have won the competition quite handily, but perhaps he felt it would be unseemly to walk off with such a large sum of money in light of his recent alliance with the Germans.

The flights at Itford Hill were not the first that Tony Fokker had made in gliders, although they seem to have been his first soaring flights. He had, in fact, made earlier experiments in which he had successfully aero towed a glider. This singular accomplishment has been largely ignored and the credit for the first aero tows given to Gottlob Espenlaub and his associates who successfully demonstrated the technique in 1927. Fokker, however, had Espenlaub & Co. beat by a good seven years when it came to aero towing and made what were quite possibly the first off-water tows as well.

Immediately following World War I, Fokker loaded what he could of his German aircraft factory on two trains and fled to his native Holland, a neutral nation, one jump ahead of Allied Control. Some well-placed sums of money are said to have helped this timely exodus. Within a short time he was again building aircraft. On the shrewd assumption that there would be a lull in the demand for military machines, Fokker turned his attention to the design of a transport and a glider.

Tony Fokker's post-WW I glider shows an obvious resemblance to the wartime D-8 fighter. Note the bit of wire hanging from the nose and the German bar cross visible on upper left-hand wing.

The glider was a very sensible little monoplane with a wingspan of 27.5 ft. and a length of 20 ft. 3 inches. Only one look was necessary to see that it was nothing else than one of the wartime D-8 fighters, *sans* Spandaus, and with the pilot position moved forward to compensate for the absent engine. Considering Fokker's cut-and-patch reputation, and his genius for improvisation, this conversion is not at all surprising.

That the glider was part of the wartime materiel whisked out of Germany was obvious from the traces of camouflage and the bar crosses of the German Air Force that were still visible on the wing. These stigmata were of little consequence during flight tests of the glider in Holland, but were the cause of a public furor when it was put on display at an aeronautical exposition in Belgium in 1920. Feeling against the Germans was still so high that Fokker was in danger of being lynched by the mob. During an exchange of diplomatic notes between Belgium and Holland, Fokker sat tight, then carted his glider back home. This occurrence might explain in part his reluctance to put on too good a show at Itford Hill.

The pilot of the Fokker glider sat in the extreme nose and was furnished with a normal control column and rudder bar. He also had control over a simple tow release made, it is said, from a pair of pliers. The undercarriage was Fokker through and through, even to the airfoil-shaped spreader bar between the wheels.

Test flights were made behind a Fokker biplane using a length of manilla rope. Because of the central location of the tow hitch there were no serious out-of-trim forces during towing. The control responses were good and the visibility excellent. The available performance specifications indicate a glide ratio of 14, a minimum sink of 3 f.p.s. and a stalling speed of 36 m.p.h. These do not quite jibe (3 f.p.s. and 36 m.p.h. giving a glide ratio of 17.5) and we can readily suspect that the sink-rate figure is the optimistic one in this instance. A never-exceed speed of 230 m.p.h. is not too difficult to accept in the light of the structural reliability of most of Fokker's airplanes.

At the time of his experiments with the glider Fokker was using a powerful motorboat as transport to and from his factory which, like so many concerns in Holland, was accessible by canal. Accordingly the glider was fitted with pontoons, the canal temporarily cleared of traffic, and more tows made. These were not the first trials of a float-equipped glider towed by motorboat, those having been made with the Voisin-Archdeacon glider of 1905, but were notable nonetheless. Altitude in the canal tows was limited by the length of the tow rope and by the nose-down pitch that resulted from the forward location of the tow hitch. The reworked pliers serving as the release mechanism were apparently functioning near their load limit during these off-water tows, so Fokker stationed a mechanic in the stern of the boat with a sharp axe—just in case. Thus he seems to have been the first to implement the guillotine as well.

Fokker is said to have found the glider extremely pleasant to fly and for a while he seems to have had some hopes of marketing it for "sport and recreation flying." Meantime the airliner project was gaining steam and orders were accumulating, so he turned his attention in that direction. Thus gliding, which would not be ready for Antony Fokker's genius for some years to come, lost the contributions of a man who might easily have advanced the sport by leaps and bounds.

## Antigravity

THERE IS A GREAT DEAL OF HUMAN SENTIMENT to the effect that the Law of Gravity, that great foundation stone of the materialist world, should be repealed. There is also a great deal of evidence that it has been, and on quite a number of occasions, too. Degravitation seems far too economic a method of getting work done, however, to be readily accepted in a culture where waste is so indispensable to progress, so the technique may have to be explored and exploited by some technologically underprivileged nations or wait till the West has so depleted its natural resources that it is forced into the use of economical modes of energy use.

The foregoing is intended neither to be idle nor cynical commentary on modern man; his methods, his morals and his manifestations are so rich in ironies and contradictions that no contrived observations are necessary to illuminate them. The material speaks for itself. If the reader doubts this, he need only acquaint himself with history. Any history will do, his own as well as another's.

As long ago as November, 1956, *Interavia* was ecstatic about the potentials of electro-gravitic research and stated that, should only one of the several lines of investigation then current prove fruitful, "gravitational acceleration as a structural, aerodynamic and medical problem will simply cease to exist." *Interavia* went on to speak of practical laboratory demonstrations: the weights of certain metals had been reduced as much as 30% by "energizing;" others had been given a negative weight, that is, made to repel gravity; disc-shaped airfoils had been successfully flown around closed air courses at high speeds when charged with up to 150,000 volts. And more, much more.

All very exciting you say. Yes, but all with a long precedent history crammed with ignorance, blindness and indifference. To illustrate this, let us go back to the years just following World War I and take up the story of a young man we shall simply identify as B. B was born in 1905 to well-to-do parents in eastern Ohio. At an early age his interests turned to space travel and this in turn led him into some experiments with a Coolidge X-ray tube which he had acquired.

At one juncture, B mounted the Coolidge tube in a very delicate balance in order to determine if it registered any variation in power when directed in different directions—and discovered that it produced thrust. As it turned out, this thrust force was not attributable to the X-rays, but to the high voltage required to generate them. It was, moreover, a *mass* force, as gravity is, not an *area* force such as magnetism. With his new-found knowledge, B constructed a primitive gravitor, a box four inches square and two feet high containing lead, glass and an insulating substance. When put on a scale and connected to 50,000 volts, B's box would register a gain or loss of one percent of its weight! Not bad for a teen-ager.

B was unaware of the scorn that pioneers must endure until he encountered it. Then he was sensitive and offended. Newspaper publicity about his work failed to get any response, and when practical demonstrations met with general apathy, B ran away from home, joined the Navy and had many and many an adventure before ultimately settling down to work again in the antigravity field. In later years he was able to demonstrate a gravitor that would, with the application of 50,000 volts, lift 110% of its own weight.

An even more fascinating and enigmatic figure than B preceded him, however. This was John Worrell Keely. Keely was born in Philadelphia in 1827, worked as a carpenter, a violinist and a magician. He spent a spell in the Rockies as a trapper but an encounter with an Indian arrow, which badly wounded him, resulted in his return to Philadelphia for recuperation. It was in 1871, at the age of 44, that Keely attracted attention with his claim that he had mastered a great new source of energy. He had, he claimed, "a device which disintegrates the etheric force that controls the atomic constitution of matter," an engine that worked on "harmonic vibrations." Perhaps more to confuse than to clarify, Keely called it the *Hydro-pneumatic-pulsating-vacue-engine.*

A few years later, in 1874, the Keely Motor Co. was formed with influential and wealthy Philadelphians as stockholders. For the next eight years a dialogue ensued between the backers, who wanted to harness Keely's force, or energy, or power, to the dollar machine, and the inventor, who gave demonstrations, but very little else. Keely collected tens of thousands of dollars, lived well, and continued his work.

Keely was kept going by the money, and the shareholders were kept going by the demonstrations. What kept the motor going was the big puzzle, although what it did was obvious enough. It was a large and complicated structure which made a humming sound and, without visible means of power input, tore heavy hausers asunder and shot a lead ball through 12 inches of oak planks.

Brute force was not all that Keely was able to demonstrate. He also showed how gravity could be overcome. In full view of a committee of his stockholders, Keely caused a small metal airship to rise and remain suspended for a full five minutes. The motive force here, as in other instances, seems to have been sound, for apparently Keely discovered the means by which audible sound waves could be built up to fantastically high frequencies. In the case of the little metal airship he began by vibrating a circular metal plate with a violin bow. The plate was connected by joined sections of silver and platinum wire to a composite bar—the launch pad—consisting of metal components machined to precise proportions.

The investors were kept content by this sort of thing for eight years, but in 1882 they had had enough promises and backed Keely up against the wall. He now agreed to tell everything to a representative of the shareholders. A Mr. Boekel, about whose qualifications we know little, was chosen. Keely kept his word, and in due time Boekel's report came. It was his opinion, he stated, that it would be improper to describe the principle involved in the operation of the motor, but that "Mr. Keely had discovered all that he had claimed."

This was not good enough for those who had financed the Keely Motor Co. They brought legal pressure to bear against the inventor, but this was insufficient to budge him. In 1888 he went to jail. He died ten years later, his final days having been cushioned by the sympathy and support of a wealthy widow.

Over a period of twenty-four years Keely had given demonstrations of one sort or another. These appear always to have been in the open and in broad daylight. He was never observed in any kind of trickery. His work seems to have been genuine beyond a doubt. Why then the unassailable resolve to keep his own counsel and not reveal his secrets to the world? Inexplicable, unless, possibly, he had discovered a power of such fearsome consequences that he preferred to take it to the grave with him rather than set it loose in a parlous and inconstant world.

* * *

If at sometime in the foreseeable future, as seems likely to happen, the marvel of antigravity is clearly demonstrated to the world in some dramatic manner, the world, should it feel generous on that occasion, may then wish to reciprocate by giving more credence than it has in the past to those accounts concerning the airships of ancient India and Atlantis which, it is related, were levitated by antigravitational forces. The world may even go so far as to believe that the Easter Island monoliths and those at Stonehenge, not to mention the great blocks used in the Egyptian pyramids, were transported and erected by the application of those universal laws of nature, and known to practitioners of the occult arts, by which the force of gravity can be neutralized, or even reversed. In the days of the building of the pyramids the stones, some of which weighed as much as 53 tons, had to be transported from as far away as the Nubian Land, which was a very very long way. It is hardly more remarkable to imagine that they were levitated by means of a lost art in which song and chanting played an important part (as those best qualified to say claim) than to envisage them being transported by any other means. Well, to each his own.

Lifting a 53-ton block of stone, it may be imagined, took a lot of chanting. For St. Joseph of Cupertino, a 17th Century Franciscan friar, all that was necessary was the characteristic little cry of "Oh!" that he emitted as he took to the air. Joseph is recorded to have made flights not only in his native Cupertino, but in Assisi, Naples and Rome as well. In this last-named city his aerial ability was witnessed by the Pope himself, Urban VIII. Seventy of Joseph's flights were subsequently sworn to by eyewitnesses.

This is the account of one such episode, a command performance as it were, set down by Father Rossi, then the Minister-General of the Franciscan order:

*"While the Lord High Admiral of Castile, Ambassador of Spain at the Vatican, was passing through Assisi in the year 1645, the custodian of the convent commanded Joseph to descend from the room into the church, where the Admiral and his lady were waiting for him, desirous of seeing him and speaking to him. To whom Joseph replied, 'I will obey, but I do not know whether I shall be able to speak to her.' And, as a matter of fact, hardly had he entered the church and raised his eyes to a statue . . . situated above the altar, when he threw himself into a flight in order to embrace its feet at a distance of twelve paces, passing over the heads of all the congregation; then, after remaining there some time, he flew back over them with his customary shrill cry, and immediately returned to his cell. The Admiral was amazed, his wife fainted away; and all the onlookers became piously terrified."*

The church set an excellent example following Joseph's death. It studied the testimony of his life for ninety years, then conferred sainthood on him.

A more contemporary case of unassisted soaring flight was the aerial performance of the late Vaslav Nijinsky. Nijinsky's *élévation,* of course, was unparalleled; he could leap nearly three feet into the air. Quite apart from this, however, he had the ability to stop at the top of his leap and then, within certain limits, to control his rate of descent, a fact which accounts for the incredible lightness with which he alighted from even his highest leaps. Nijinsky's wife, Romola, said her husband admitted to her that he simply took a leap, held his breath and stayed up, that he felt supported by the air, that he could come down slower or quicker as he desired, and that he could not understand why other dancers couldn't do the same!

In one form or another breath control, or breathing rhythm seems to be an essential element in levitation phenomena. Nijinsky could outdo even Caruso in the matter of filling his lungs with air and evidently rivaled the Italian tenor in control as well. The dancer was an avowed student of the occult and perhaps he took part of his technique from the legendary Tibetan *lung-gom-pa,* those phenomenal individuals who can traverse hundreds of miles at surprizingly high speeds. The *lung-gom-pa* cover the ground in a series of extended leaps, rebounding lightly each time they touch the earth, and sometimes going on their way completely independent of the ground. Some, indeed, are reputed to wear chains, lest they float away entirely!

What is necessary for this particular sort of levitation is the activation of the heart, or anahata chakram. To achieve this a proselyte, it is said, must practice special breathing exercises for three years and three months, both in darkness and seclusion. To maintain the requisite lightness of body during the long runs or glides, the *lung-gom-pa* must recite a mystical formula to the accompaniment of the breathing and to the rhythm of the strides.

Like many another metaphysical matter, this one too has been subjected to laboratory analysis. The experiment is quite simple, really, and you may recall from your own experience the parlor game in which, after a session of unison breathing, a seated person is lifted by two (or four) others using their index fingers under the armpits and behind the knees. If you have played the game, perhaps you recall the lightness of the body being lifted and the ease with which four relatively weak digits managed so heavy a load. Perhaps it did not occur to you that anything more than a *sensation* of lightness was involved, that there was a *phenomenon* as well. It did occur to Dr. Hereward Carrington, the noted investigator of psychical phenomena, however, and this is what he observed when he placed five people on the platform of a large self-registering scale and had them begin lifting:

*"On the first lift . . . the needle of the dial had fallen to 660 pounds (the combined weight was found previously to be 712 pounds), a loss of 52 pounds. On the second lift there was an*

*apparent loss of 52 pounds; on the third lift of 60 pounds; and on the fourth lift of 60 pounds; and on the fifth lift of 60 pounds. No gain of weight was any time recorded (owing to muscular exertion); invariably there was a loss which, however, slowly returned to normal as the subject was held for some considerable time in the air."*

Over to you.

## Taylor McDaniel's Flexible Flying Machines

GENERATIONS of gliders have come and gone since Sir George Cayley wafted his coachman down the hill at Brompton Hall in the middle of the 19th Century. Most have belonged to families that, if not completely respectable, at least did not put any serious strain on the canons of convention. Inevitably, however, there have been the mavericks, the bastard children and the prodigal sons. Among these latter must certainly be placed an odd pair of inflatable gliders designed and built by one Taylor McDaniel.

McDaniel, like his flexible flying machines, seems to have a wanderer in untrodden ways—and to have had plenty of bounce. He was born in Tappahanack, Va. in 1892, but left home at an early age. His roustabout existence took him first across the United States, then to South America. He is reported to have traversed that continent from west to east on foot, to have retired from an early attempt to begin air service in Brazil using World War I surplus aircraft when his partner, "an Italian air ace named Bertoni" was killed in a test flight, to have married, tried his hand at gold mining and finally bossed a cattle ranch for his wife's uncle, Ordone Accorsihas, until revolutionary activity made it impossible to continue shipping meat by train.

At length McDaniel returned to the U.S. with his wife and, after a few years in Philadelphia, settled in Washington D.C. It was here, during the winter of 1930, that he set about building the McDaniel Rubber Glider No. 1.

The idea of an inflatable glider, as revolutionary as it may have seemed even in 1930, did not originate with Taylor Mc-

Daniel. As early as 1912 a British Lieutenant, Dennistoun Burney, had designed a collapsible aircraft which was to have been made of rubberized fabric, stowed in the compartment of a submarine, inflated when required for action, and be so equipped that it could take off from water and provide an observation point above its mother vessel.

Whether or not McDaniel was stimulated by Lt. Burney's conception is impossible to say; he had, however, lived a good proportion of his adult life in one of the world's principal rubber-producing areas, and he had had a business associate, a man who knew how to fly, killed in the crash of a conventional wood-and-wire airplane. More than likely these were the elements that contributed most to McDaniel's unorthodox approach to aircraft construction.

Each wing half of the McDaniel rubber glider was comprised of three spanwise inflatable tubes covered with fabric and braced with wire. The forward part of the fuselage was a simple frame

Taylor McDaniel (at left in photo opposite) pauses during work on frame and main tubular members of the first inflatable glider. Initial flight, with Bergling as pilot ended satisfactorily.

resembling that of a primary glider; the rear fuselage another wire-braced inflatable tube. Exact specifications do not seem to have survived, but we can probably accept a wing area of 110 sq. ft. and an empty weight of 125 lbs. as being close enough for our purposes.

The glider was crude in the extreme, particularly as concerned control surfaces. It didn't have any. The provisions for control, such as they were, consisted of linkage and wires to warp the wings and a method of deflecting the tail surfaces by pinching the tail tube just ahead of the stabilizer. These nevertheless sufficed and the glider did fly—once.

This event came upon a hard, cold January day in 1931 at Washington's old Hoover Field. McDaniel, who was a strapping great fellow, outweighed his elastic glider by the better part of 100 lbs. With him aboard, consequently, the glider was too nose heavy to leave the ground and after the first few tries, attempts to get it airborne were abandoned.

At this critical point the designer was fortunate in obtaining the services of one Joseph C. Bergling—to whom, the author should quickly add, he is indebted for most of the details of this account and for the photographs as well. Bergling's virtues were as follows: He was a glider pilot, instructor for the D.C. Air Legion Glider Club, as a matter of fact; he was small, weighing in at 155 lbs; he was willing, willing enough, as it turned out, to do the job for kicks. And that was about all he got out of it.

Kick number one came when Bergling made a successful initial flight. This was accomplished by auto tow and was aided at the outset by a pair of wingtip runners who stabilzed the glider during the 50 ft. or so of its ground run. The right wing dropped when the tips were released, but Bergling retrieved it and hauled the glider skyward using back stick.

At an altitude of 60 or 70 ft. the pilot slipped the tow rope from about the newel on the front of the skid and began the quick trip back to earth. This was accomplished with the stick full against the rear stop and the glider in a mushing stall. The machine was moving so slowly when it hit the ground that it skidded barely five feet.

Kick number two was a different sort of kick altogether. At the commencement of the second flight the wingtip runners let go somewhat prematurely, possibly a bit overconfident from the success of the first trial. The right wingtip dropped again, and again Bergling corrected for it, pulling the glider into a climbing attitude as he did so. Instead of stabilizing, however, the glider now began to act like an unmanageable kite on a string. It swung to the left, then sharply over to the right and smartly into the ground.

From an altitude of perhaps 50 ft., still tethered to the tow car, the rubber glider, the pilot sitting exposed on the fragile wooden frame out front, dove directly into the hard January ground of Hoover Field—and for a brief moment it looked as if Joseph C. Bergling had gone the way of McDaniel's erstwhile aeronautical playmate, Bertoni. But a moment later he stood up, "to show them I was okay" he admitted later, and waved. The glider, which had crumpled on impact, thrashed about a bit and resumed its former shape. Except for a broken wire or two, it was in flyable condition. A most remarkable demonstration.

* * *

Despite the Taylor-made proof that the glider would fly, and the air-tight demonstration that it would crash and spare the pilot, nothing came of the McDaniel Rubber Glider No. 1. The years of the Great Depression were not good ones for investment in general and rather poor for investment in rubber gliders in particular. It was the day of elastic securities, not elastic airplanes.

Still frames from a newsreel clip show Bergling's second flight in McDaniel's inflatable glider. The pilot survived the crash nicely, immediately stood up to wave to the distant newsmen.

McDaniel was inflated enough by his initial success, however, to want to pursue the matter further. Consequently he built a second and very fanciful glider employing larger numbers of

The completed framework of Taylor McDaniel's second elastic excursion module, complete with a set of flappers for auto-propulsion. The gentleman standing near the left wing-tip is Ernie Pyle who covered the Washington aviation beat at the time.

tubes, but of smaller diameter. Ernie Pyle, who covered the aviation beat in Washington in those days, said it resembled a cross between a Texas Longhorn steer and a turtle dove. It never flew.

Bergling, a pressman by profession, still lives on the outskirts of Washington. McDaniel drifted into obscurity and died in 1952, at the age of 60, having spent the last years of his life as a watchman in a warehouse. Bergling, who saw him only infrequently in the years following their association in the glider business, claims McDaniel died of a broken heart.

## Tows to the Stratosphere

OF ALL THE spectacular feats performed with gliders in the years before World War II, perhaps none was more sensational than the stratospheric tows performed by a team of Russian pilots and technicians in 1936 and 1937. To pursue the investigation of soaring conditions at high altitudes an ingenious glider train was improvised consisting of a twin-engine military transport and two gliders, one a single-place, the other two-place. The transport and the two-place glider were both equipped with winches and wire, the wire from the winch in the transport being connected to the two-place glider, and that of the two-place glider attached to the single-place glider.

This odd assemblage took off from an airfield near Moscow in good order and circled twice around the city while climbing to 15,000 ft., the operational limit of the tug. At this height the two-place glider was kited up another 3,000 ft. by playing out the wire on the winch in the transport. In its turn the single-place glider was kited to an altitude of 21,000 ft. At the conclusion of this unusual aerial episode the gliders released and returned to the airfield from whence the tow had begun.

The Russians were evidently quite satisfied with the results of their early tests, for they announced that they would make subsequent attempts to reach even greater heights with gliders. These trials, too, were successful. On June 30th, 1937, Fydoroff, a pilot whose name figures prominently in Russian gliding, was towed to an altitude of 28,050 ft. With this start Fydoroff is said to have soared to an altitude of 39,946 ft.

## Vignettes from The Perilous and Poignant Past (No. 66)

THE TIME WAS the summer of 1953; the place, Yugoslavia, during the annual national soaring championships. The protagonist is "Pirat" Gehriger, one of Switzerland's foremost glider pilots:

"Flying a borrowed Weihe on the last day, Gehriger was on tow during the retrieve when two other tug-glider combinations flew up alongside and were flying in formation the last 100 miles back to the base. Ann and Lorne Welch were in one of these. They would arrive in good time for the grand farewell party.

"Gehriger lit a cigarette and threw the match out the window —he thought. Shortly afterwards the cockpit began to fill with smoke and some research revealed that the feather cushion on which Gehriger was sitting was on fire. The smell was appalling and the smoke thick, but feathers are difficult to extinguish. With the stick between his knees, Gehriger tried to crush the flames by hand, using a supply of dried fruit left over from lunch to smother the smouldering feathers.

"In the meantime the evolutions of the centre glider in the sextet of aircraft were remarkable, but the other glider pilots saw no signs of the fire. Gehriger realized that the sensible course was to release and land—and miss the party. He decided to take a chance. Nearer home the smoke began again—this time from somewhere further down or behind. If the bottom of the fuselage were on fire the metal stick should be getting hot. Gehriger's hands were, however, too burnt to be able to detect any warmth. The seat of the new fire soon revealed itself when Gehriger's parachute straps suddenly pulled away, smouldering.

"Before anything more serious happened the base was in sight and the gliders pulled off. It was early evening and the other two circled lazily, but Gehriger's Weihe—brakes out—went down steeply to land. The parachute had been destroyed and there were two large holes burnt through the sides of the fuselage. Gehriger thinks it lucky that the other pilots didn't notice these or he might have been signalled to pull off and miss the party!"

—*Sailplane and Gliding*

## Flying Folly

SOARING PEOPLE like to think of themselves as superior types, just as sailing people, or skiing people, or just any kind of people do. If being superior, however, means being above all manner of damn foolishness, including those very special instances of very extra special damn foolishness that cause one to suspect the intervention of some special power, then soaring people must abrogate their claims and be content merely to be thought of as people who, despite some special talents, are simply the same people doing something different.

To support this case we present the reader with what may at first appear to be a thoroughly remarkable sequence of events. Thus: the towplane and glider are hooked up and ready to begin a flight. The wingtip of the glider is lifted from the ground to a level position. The tow pilot shoves the throttle forward and commences the takeoff.

All normal operating procedure — except that the glider, in this case, is empty! Little matter that the hook-up at the glider end should never be made until the pilot is in the ship and ready to go, nor that he should release if he decides for some reason to quit the cockpit, nor that the wingtip should be left at rest on the ground until a specific command is given to lift it, nor that the diligent tow pilot keeps his eye on his charges and does not permit this sort of thing to happen. Little matter, for the pilotless glider on tow is a standard repertory item, about as dependable as the Sunday sailor who drills a hole in the bottom of his boat to let the water drain out without beaching it first.

This sort of story will get barely a nod from the *cognoscenti*. They've been around too long and seen too much. They'll remember half a dozen instances, up to and including the time a 62-ft. Hotspur was towed off without its pilot. To get *their* attention you will have to have a very special story, one intimating the intervention of genius, like the time that . . .

In the beginning all was in order. True, it had required a bit more than a normal expenditure of energy to get things ready, there being only the two parties on hand to make preparations. But now both pilots were strapped in, the tow pilot in his Newbury *Eon,* a low-wing monoplane, the glider pilot in his *Olympia,* canopy closed. Then the *Eon's* engine stopped.

The pilot of the tug apparently did not want to inconvenience the pilot of the glider with another long hike to the *Eon* and back, just to swing a propeller once; and the *Olympia* pilot, having already gone to considerably more trouble than glider pilots are accustomed to in the process of getting airborne, was apparently content to sit tight. So, despite the fact the law forbids it, and that common sense has a great deal to say against it as well, the tug pilot got out of the pit, went around to the nose, and began to crank, possibly a bit comforted by the anchor effect provided by the occupied glider at the far end of the line.

The *Eon,* however, was stubborn, so the impatient pilot, still adhering to the rules of the game, walked back around to the cockpit and opened the throttle a little more. The *Eon* still resisted, but the pilot persisted still. Finally the throttle was opened to the point where the *Eon* had to capitulate. The engine roared into life. The pilot jumped out of the way of the spinning prop, as required, and dutifully went on to the next item on the agenda — grabbing the wingtip and holding on for dear life.

Up to this point there is really very little in the way of novelty in this account beyond the fact that the *Eon* pilot, in addition to the standard performance at the wingtip, was obliged to jump rope with each revolution of the airplane.

Now, however, it was time for the glider pilot, who thus far had had a very choice view of the events, and had successfully resisted whatever urge he may have felt to give a hand, to add what he could to the proceedings. All that was required of him to turn this rather prosaic little comedy into a masterpiece of mortal folly, was to upstrap himself and get out of the *Olympia* without releasing the towline.

This he obligingly did. With his weight in the glider no longer serving as anchor, the testy towplane could not be restrained. Pilotless it took off, and pilotless the glider followed.

Neither the *Eon* nor the *Olympia* got very far. The story, however, has come a long way. It got to the author third or fourth hand, and he has not hesitated to add his embellishments to those accumulated in transit. So the saga of the *Eon* and the *Olympia* may not have happened *exactly* as recounted above, but the essentials, we feel certain, are substantially as recounted. In fact, only one important detail was omitted. The towpilot's name was Mr. Towgood.

# 3

## The Lower End of the Scale

FOR THE MOST PART soaring pilots are preoccupied with the higher end of the performance scale, the area where all compromises are made in the interest of obtaining the ultimate results possible. The compromises are many and tend to increase with every advance in performance. Among them are the greater complexity of the modern sailplane and the care it demands, higher landing speeds, mounting expenses, and the increasing degree to which the pilot becomes isolated from the *sensations of flight*. One or more of these considerations have led to developments in the opposite direction, specifically to the matter of achieving flight with the barest minimum of means.

Over the years, and for reasons as diverse as the means employed, people have been guiding themselves through the air in some remarkably scanty collections of rod and fabric. Perhaps the patron saint of those committed to flying with nothing beyond the absolute essentials was the Dutchman, Reinhold Platz. Platz was evidently impressed by the parallel between sailing and soaring, for he borrowed the planform of boat sails, one set of sails to a side, the intersecting masts becoming the main spar, as the basis of the design of his gliding apparatus. The operator sat at the junction of the two mast-spars, relying on the mainsails to supply lift, and using the co-joined

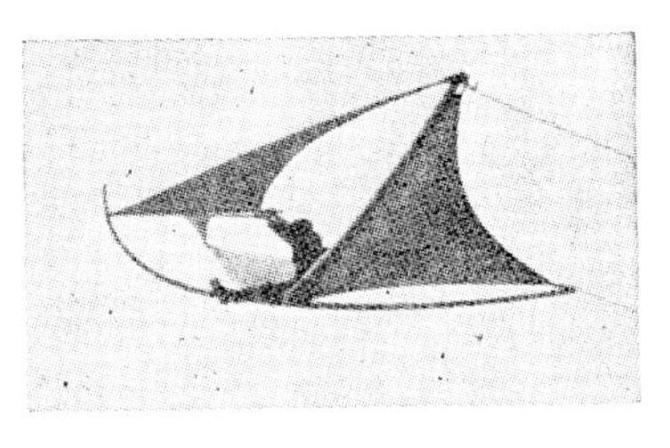

jibs, which went on ahead, as his means of achieving longitudinal control.

There is an historic photograph of Platz, probably taken in 1924, which shows him peddling his bicycle along one of the cobblestone streets of his native Scheveningen with his glider, the Platz I, neatly rolled up and perched on his shoulder. He appears to be a slightly stout gentleman for piloting such a glider, but he has a very happy smile on his face, a certain indication of the rightness of his cause.

That cause was not picked up when Reinhold Platz dropped it. The main line of glider development, centered around activities on the Wasserkuppe, was toward the mastery of the high-performance glider, and those involved in it were having enough trouble getting complicated gliders to fly to bother with simple ones. Before any reaction could take place there would have to be a lot more action, which of course, there was.

Years passed, and one and another innovator came forward with proposals of one kind or another — sailwings, inflatable structures, ultra-small gliders — but few of these proved to have the combination of convenience and (relative) safety of the simple flightsail design of Francis Rogallo. Rogallo's wing (see cover) consists of two leading edge spars set at approximately 45° angles to a longitudinal keel. A cross bar holds these members together and a sail of suitably non-porous material attached to them fulfills the role of wing.

Thus far, shifting the center of gravity has proven to be the most suitable method of steering the Rogallo. For this reason it makes an excellent hang glider. In Southern California, where the populace seems temperamentally disposed to try just about anything, a number of these have been built and flown using frameworks of bamboo or aluminum and thin polyethelene sheet for sails. Properly handled they have provided a great deal of fun, the sensation of flight *in excelsis,* and a minimum of morphological mayhem.

The adaptability of Mr. Rogallo's design to their special needs was not long lost on the parachutists who had been for sometime on the lookout for increased means of "increased horizontal displacement," or what glider pilots, on a higher octave, call L/D. A glide ratio of three, which a chute patterned on the

Rogallo wing offered them, was better than anything the sky-divers then had and promised much greater precision in jumping, and particularly in spot landings, than they could have hoped for previously.

The day will unquestionably come, and it probably isn't too far off, when the parachutists discover that the increased maneuverability and higher-than-parity glide ratios of their new chutes will permit them to thermal their rudimentary gliders and set out on cross-country flights.

There are many more instances of parachutes and parachutists being carried off by updrafts than might be imagined. Certain of these cases, as when several German pilots bailed out of their demolished gliders in a cu-nim and were frozen to death, are tragic, but there is at least one case on record of a quite respectable "flight" in a parachute. This occurred in the U.S.S.R., a nation passionately devoted to parachuting, probably in the spring of 1955. Shortly after opening his chute, and at an altitude of about 2,500 ft., jumper Joseph Adamuk was caught in a strong thermal which carried him to a height of almost 10,000 ft. When he finally landed, Adamuk had been airborne for 1 hr. 55 mins. No distance for this inadvertent excursion, but in all likelihood the jumper landed some distance from his take-off site.

Still further in the direction of simplicity, which is the direction in which we're moving, are the experiences of a Cape Cod park ranger and of another Russian parachutist. The ranger, Ping Crawford by name, was making a check of erosion on a section of beach near the village of Wellfleet during a gale when circumstances precipitated his brief aeronautical career. The gale in question was so intense that Crawford was forced to crawl the 30 feet between the shelter he occupied and the cliff edge. When he attempted to peer over the edge the wind billowed his poncho, picked him up, and rolled him back to where he'd begun.

Not having been damaged by his unexpected solo, and being a sporting type, Crawford worked his way back to the cliff edge for a second try. This time he jumped off, spreading his poncho as he did so. The result was a launch to six feet, a duration (more or less) of five seconds and a cross-country hop, albeit backwards, of some 30 ft.

Crawford experimented further, now from a point down the cliff face. By deploying his poncho there, he discovered, he would promptly be carried to the top of the cliff again. With time he was able to effect a certain measure of control over his flights by manipulating the poncho. Whether this contributed anything to erosion studies is hard to say, but we'll bet that Mr. Crawford kept a weather eye out for gale warnings from that day forward.

The flight of the Russian parachutist — for he did not pursue the matter beyond a single essay — was also a spur-of-the-moment affair and was not made in a parachute, but by means similar to those employed by Ping Crawford. That G. Ochepkov, a Soviet mechanic assigned to an Mi.4 helicopter at the time this incident took place, was a parachutist is, furthermore, only incidental to the story. As a former Air Force wireless operator he had made 17 jumps. He had also apparently mastered his fear of heights and falling for when, one winter day, while on flight duty, he inadvertently opened a door of the Mi.4 and was suddenly ejected from the machine, he was able to cope with the situation.

To call Ochepkov cool would be understating the case. There he was, at something over 1,000 ft., with no chute and a forest below as the only likely landing spot. Nonetheless he took immediate steps to direct his destiny and wrest what small measure of victory he could from circumstances as black as the forbidding limbs of the lifeless trees below. Quickly he opened his quilted jacket and, falling face downwards, grasped the flaps. Thus prepared, he "glided" into a small glade in the forest where he fell into six feet of snow. The snow buffered his fall and greatly eased the landing. Although Ochepkov briefly lost consciousness at the moment of impact, probably as the result of shock, he was later able to climb into the helicopter by himself.

## Mid-Air Dismantling

IT IS NOT very often that a pilot takes a glider aloft for the specific purpose of destroying it, although the post-mortem of many an accident would seem to provide evidence to the contrary. Just such an instance, however, took place in Russia during the period of intense experimentation prior to World War II that also produced such novelties as long-distance air trains and triple-decker stratospheric tows.

The Russians were not being either frivolous nor imprudent in this case of aerial annihilation; what they sought was empirical test data related to the effects of high-speed flight on flutter in flying surfaces. Consequently they so modified an experimental glider so as to enable the pilot, by operating a sequence of release mechanisms, to shed one surface after another in flight. The locale for the experiment was Koktebel in the Crimea, the pilot a 21-year-old lad named Sergei Anokhim.

Anokhim was towed to an altitude of 7,000 ft. from whence he began his precipitous plummet towards the earth. One by one he let the surfaces tear away until the ship was stripped clean. After falling an additional 3,000 ft. in the bare fuselage Anokhim bailed out and parachuted to a landing with information intended to aid in the construction of stronger and more efficient gliders.

## Vignettes from The Perilous and Poignant Past (No. 82)

THE TIME WAS December of 1965; the place, a stretch of river in the vicinity of Slatington, Pa. The protagonist is Thomas G. Beltz, then a 14-year-old 1-26 pilot:

"I hadn't anticipated much sink because of the dead lift. I'm sure that if there had not been as much as there was, I would easily have made Slatington. When I realized that making the airport was out of the question, the big decision came upon me: should I land on a rock and debris infested island, a rocky shore full of railroad ties, holes and boulders, or the river? The river was my choice.

"By this time I had about fifty feet over the water, so I drove it down close to the water, indicating 74 m.p.h. I glided on down the river and put my wheel into the water, indicating about 50 m.p.h. Then, spotting an outcropping of rock dead ahead, I did the only logical thing and climbed over it. I went back into the river indicating 40 m.p.h., and as the shore was coming closer, I put the whole main bottom of the glider in. Slowed down to about 25 m.p.h., I hit the bank of the river.

"Luckily for me, there had been another drought this past summer and the main river bank was about thirty feet above. But at this time the river was so low that a small bank had been established about a foot above the river level. This small area had boulders and shale outcroppings, railroad ties, holes and a lot of other junk. I hit this bank and with two loud bangs (one hitting the bank and the other when I made my final stop), finally came to rest between a boulder and a great shale outcropping, my right wing resting on the latter.

"So ends my flight, with a much higher respect for the Schweizer 1-26."

—*The 1-26 Log*

## Great Balls of Fire

SCIENCE (with a capital S) sometimes appears as the keeper of a vast zoo destined eventually to receive one specimen of every phenomenon under the sun, but a zoo more notable for the variable morphology of many of its existing specimens—and its acres of empty cages—than for the displays it confidently exhibits as fully and immutably finished.

The aviary in Science's zoo is particularly rich in rare items. One of its more arresting displays is an empty cage marked:

### GREAT BALLS OF FIRE
*(Ball Lightning)*

Ball lightning has been observed by many people in many places for many years. It has been reported in the great and not-so-great scientific journals of the world for centuries, as, for example: "Balls of fire"—Norway, 1752; "Fire ball in the sky, apparent size of the moon"—Naples, 1821; "Huge ball of green fire"—London, 1877; "A large triple-headed fire ball"—Warmsley, England, 1912.

Sightings have occurred just before earthquakes, and just after them, and the phenomenon is common during electrical storms. The fire balls drop to earth or they plunge into the sea; they hang motionless in the sky; they leave a trace of viscous or resinous matter; they drop down the chimney as if coming for dinner. About all the wisest of men can say is what they *do*, because nobody seems to be able to say what they *are*. I myself tend to the belief that what they are are discarnate spirits, firey, but rarely malevolent, out for an evening's walk, relatively speaking.

For the most part fireballs seem to be unusually solicitous of human life and property, particularly considering the degree of damage they might do. They do render existence almost unbearable at times, however, as was the case during October and November of 1902 where there were intensive falls of fireballs over Australia. They started fires in every district in Victoria and in Sydney business was stopped and people went stumbling about with lanterns in the blackness. At night the landscape was illuminated by great balls of fire, one the apparent size of the sun.

Perhaps the case in Australia was simply one of mob violence among an otherwise respectable bunch of individuals. In any event most reports are significantly less cataclysmic, if scarcely less curious. There are instances on record of fire balls entering houses by open windows and posing themselves near individuals, or entering closed rooms through keyholes and of pursuing people around their own houses, but without harming them, in an almost sentient manner.

* * *

Two remarkable instances of the behavior of ball lightning are given in Guy Murchie's excellent book, *Song of the Sky.* One relates to a ball of fire which appeared in the room of a house in the city of Marseille, France, in the year 1898 and approached a small girl sitting on a table. This ball, which was surrounded by a glowing haze, rose and circled the terrified little girl twice, then darted up the chimney and exploded with "an appalling crash that shook the entire house."

The second instance was that of a fire ball which hit the ground between two cottages in an English village. This bifurcating specimen broke up, each half entering one of the cottages via the chimney. In the first instance the fireball descended directly into the cellar of the house and exploded, destroying a valuable chicken brooder.

In the neighboring cottage the ball quietly made its way through a room in which a man was reading to a boy, leaving them both untouched. It then burned a small hole in the floor through which it dropped into the sheepfold below. Here, either by design or happenstance, it killed five full-grown sheep, but spared the young lambs that jumped about in terror. This done, it squeezed past the shepherd's son who had meanwhile arrived at the door of the sheepfold, left the house and disappeared across an adjoining field "almost as if it had a mind of its own."

## Vignettes from The Perilous and Poignant Past (No. 162)

THE TIME WAS the first day of spring in the year 1934; the place, Norwich Airport, Norwich, New York; the protagonist, Lieutenant Brownie Temple, U.S.N.

"The thrill of the day was provided by Temple. It seems that the bolt on the Franklin had been adjusted for airplane tow with parachute and the slackness of the belt was not noticed when Temple got into the cockpit. About fifty feet from the ground in a steep climb behind the car the tow line broke. Temple instinctively shoved the stick forward with such speed and impetus that in going 'over the hump' he was thrown out of the seat. The belt was so slack that Temple knocked the nose cowl (scoop) loose and it promptly settled over his head like a candle snuffer. While trying to haul himself back into the seat with the aid of the stick, he was handicapped further by having the rubber grip pull off. Then he discovered that instead of straddling the stick, both legs were on the same side of the stick.

"Temple sought to control the scoop with one hand and the stick with the other and he finally made a passable down-wind landing. The only damage was a broken rib and trailing edge in the wing tip, a result of the final group loop."

—*The Gliding and Soaring Bulletin*

## Big Gliders

THE FIRST GLIDERS with large wingspans were built in the early 1920's at about the time slope soaring began on the Wasserkuppe and as a consequence of the realization of the role that high aspect ratio played in glider performance. Gottlob Espenlaub—*Espie,* the gypsy—led the way. In 1922, the year after the *Vampyr* appeared at the Rhoen, he built what was, in effect, a 17-meter version of that famous sailplane. The next year the Darmstadt group introduced the *Konsul* with a span of 18.7 meters. Although this has tended to be about the upper limit for single-place designs—and happens to be exactly the span of the modern BS-1—larger gliders are by no means uncommon. Two

of note, each quite unique in its way, are the D-30 *Cirrus* and the *Horton III,* both 20-meter (66-ft.) span sailplanes.

The largest of all the single-place designs ever built was the *Austria,* made in 1930 by the engineer Kupper for Kronfeld. Although this monstrous machine probably achieved a very low rate of sink, as desired, its 30-meter (98-ft.) span made transport, ground handling, and towing, troublesome. At one point, in fact, Kronfeld had to employ a unique double-tow arrangement in which the towing aircraft was supplemented by an automobile, with its own line, that helped get the *Austria* moving. Once the ship was free of the ground, the auto tow-rope was released and the airplane finished the tow on its own.

The large spans proved a problem in the air as well as on the ground. The velocity differential between the wing-tips in circling flight, particularly at slower speeds, complicated even further matters that had not, at that time, been satisfactorily resolved. Wings seldom met very high standards as far as structural strength, rigidity and flutter characteristics were concerned, a consequence that led to a number of mishaps. Kronfeld made his first parachute descent from a glider the day the *Austria* broke up in cloud.

Two-place gliders naturally tend to be larger than their single-place counterparts, and naturally would be, except for the *Austria.* Some noteworthy pre-war types were the German D-31, a machine almost as remarkable in its way as its predecessor, the fantastic D-30. Despite its 65.7-ft. span and 210 sq.ft. of wing area, this ship had an equipped weight of only 396 lbs. The Russion *Stakhonovitch,* which introduced sweep-forward as a solution to rear cockpit visibility, was somewhat larger (66.2 ft.). Still larger were the German designs *Sturm* (82 ft.) and *Obs* (85.3 ft.). *Obs* had 408 sq.ft. of wing area (about equal to four *Libelles*) and a gross weight of 1410 lbs. (about equal to two *Libelles*). It had a gull wing with a straight trailing edge and high taper ratio toward the extremities. It was not a particularly at-

A Horton VI, built in Germany during the war years, confiscated by the Allies, and eventually turned over to the Northrop Aeronautical Institute for study. Despite its 78-ft. span, the ship had a root chord of only 3 ft. 4 in. Spar was of wood, empty weight 750 lbs.

# FIFTY SIGNIFICANT DATES IN

**1809** ——— Flight of world's first full-size, modern-configuration airplane, with ballast, by Sir George Cayley, at Brompton Hall, Yorkshire, England.

**1857** ——— Launch from a towed cart and brief flight of the first Le Bris glider on a stretch of beach near Trefeuntec, France, with the designer as pilot.

**1883, Aug. 28** What is alleged to have been the first controlled flight in a heavier-than-air machine, by John J. Montgomery, at Wheeler Hill, Otay Mesa, California.

**1891** ——— The beginning, with the start of methodical and consistent controlled flight by Otto Lilienthal, on a slope near Berlin, of the modern air age.

**1896, Aug. 9** The death of Lilienthal following a crash on the Gollenberg, near Rhinow, Germany, in one of his "Standard" (No. 11) gliders.

**1896, Sept.** — First tests, by Octave Chanute, at Miller Dunes, Indiana, of a trussed glider that was the forerunner of generations of double-bay biplanes.

**1901, Sept. 18** Address by Wilbur Wright before the Western Society of Engineers, in Chicago, in which he precisely described the principles of soaring flight.

**1902** ——— Nearly 1,000 glides, including one of 622½ feet, lasting 26 seconds, by Wilbur and Orville Wright during their third season at Kitty Hawk, N.C.

**1905, March 16** Daniel Maloney lands in an apple tree in a Montgomery tandem monoplane following release from a balloon at 800 ft. and a controlled descent.

**1909, June 27** A soaring flight, with pronounced gain of height, by Eric Gordon England, in a Weiss tailless glider, at Mt. Amberley, Sussex, England.

**1910, July 15** The start of a two-month gliding encampment, by a group of Darmstadt schoolboys under the leadership of Hans Guttermuth, on Wasserkuppe.

**1911, Oct. 24** Orville Wright, testing a device for maintaining automatic stability, establishes a world soaring record of 9 minutes 45 seconds at Kitty Hawk.

**1911, Oct. 31** The death of Montgomery, at Evergreen Valley, near San Jose, California, following a stall and sideslip into the ground in his 1911 monoplane.

**1914, July 7** An early thermal flight, claimed to have been made by the French sergeant Grasset in a Dorand-Anzani biplane near Issy-les-Moulineaux, France.

**1920, July 15 to Sept. 15** Beginning of the post-World War I gliding competitions on the Wasserkuppe, fruit of the labors of Oscar Ursinus, editor of *Flugsport*.

**1920, Aug. 15** A soaring flight at the Wasserkuppe of 2:30, with two passes over his launch point, by Peschke, flying the tailless *Weltensegler*.

**1921, June 1** Award of the first C badge to Wolfgang Klemperer for a flight of 1.83 km. made in his *Schwarzer Teufel* on September 4, 1920.

**1921, Sept. 13** Frederic Harth establishes a new world duration record of 21:30 flying one of his dynamic soaring gliders on the Heidelstein in the Rhon Mountains.

**1922, Aug.** — The beginning of organized gliding in France with the First Experimental Congress of Combegrasse.

**1922, Aug. 18** First soaring flight in excess of one hour (1:06) by Arthur Martens in the Hannover *Vampyr*, on the Wasserkuppe.

**1922, Oct. 16** Start of the first British soaring contest, at Itford Hill, South Downs, England; won by Maneyrol with a flight of 3 hours 21 minutes.

**1923, Jan. 3** First soaring flight to exceed five hours by the Frenchman Thoret, in an Hanriot biplane (with engine stopped) at Biskra, Algeria.

**1923, Sept.** — First Russian national Contest at Usun-Syrt, near Feodosia in the Crimea. Best flight of the meet; 1 hour 2 minutes by Youngmeister.

**1926, Aug. 12** Max Kegel's flight of 55 km., in a sailplane of his own construction, on a storm front, from the Wasserkuppe to Gompertshausen, Germany.

**1928, Feb. 28** Beginning of two-day "Glider Carnival" in Long Beach, California.

# THE HISTORY OF WORLD GLIDING

**1929, May 15** Kronfeld flies 102.2 km. along the Teutoberger Wald in his Wein for the first soaring flight in history to exceed 100 kilometers.

**1929, Aug. 25** Johannes Nehring makes the first altitude gain in excess of 1,000 meters (1,209 m.) at Bergstrasse, Germany in a Darmstadt sailplane.

**1930, Jan. 31** Ralph S. Barnaby drops from the dirigible *Los Angeles* at an altitude of 3,000 ft. in his Pruefling secondary glider.

**1930, Oct. 2** The first blue-sky thermal flight, 53 kilometers from Elmira to Apalachin, New York, by Wolf Hirth in his *Musterle*.

**1931, Jan.** — Joseph C. Bergling makes the first flights in the McDaniel rubber glider No. 1 at Hoover Field in Washington, D. C.

**1931, Feb. 15** The first Silver badge awarded to Robert Kronfeld, but later transferred to Wolf Hirth on account of Kronfeld being a Jew.

**1931, March 3** First systematic soaring flights in the Moazagotl wave over the village of Hirschberg in Selesia, Germany.

**1931, June 20** First glider crossing of the English Channel, by Robert Kronfeld, to and from St. Inglevert, France, in his *Wien* using 10,000-ft. tows.

**1931, July 1-2** Initial meeting, in London, of what was to become ISTUS, the *Comité Internationale d'Études du Vol sans Moteur*.

**1932, May 10** The Soaring Society of America incorporated in the State of Delaware with Warren E. Eaton as its first president.

**1934, Feb. 19** First gain of altitude of more than 3,000 meters (4,350 m.) made by Heini Dittmar at Rio de Janeiro flying a *Condor*.

**1935, July 29** First soaring flight(s) to exceed 500 km. by four German pilots, Otto Braeutigam, Hans Heinemann, Rudolf Oeltzscher and Ernst Steinhoff.

**1937, June 30** A towed flight to 28,050 ft., from which he subsequently soared to an altitude of 39,946 ft., by the Soviet pilot Fydoroff, near Moscow.

**1938, Jan. 1** World's first Gold badge awarded to the German Heini Dittmar.

**1939, April 22** First soaring flight across the English Channel by G. H. Stephenson, who flew a Kirby *Gull* from Dunstable to near Boulogne, France.

**1939, July 6** Olga Klepikova establishes an absolute world distance record of 749 km. (465 mi.) which was to stand for 22 years.

**1940, May** — Attack by the Germans on Fort Eben Emael on the Albert Canal in Belgium, the first overt military use of the glider.

**1944, Jan. 1** Heavy Industries formed in Colditz Castle, a German POW keep, for the purpose of building an escape glider, the Colditz Cock.

**1945, Oct. 15** All-American Aviation begins a lobster run from Hull, Mass., to Bendix Airport, N. J., using a converted TG-3A for transport.

**1950, July 1** First three-Diamond badge awarded to Johnny Robinson, effective with the completion of his goal flight.

**1951, Aug. 5** First distance flight of over 500 miles (535.169 mi.) by Richard H. Johnson, from Odessa, Texas, to Salina, Kansas, in the sailplane RJ-5.

**1952, July 12** Philip Wills crowned World Soaring Champion, for his victory in a Slingsby *Sky*, following the 4th World Gliding Championships, Madrid, Spain.

**1956, July 13** Paul B. MacCready Jr. flies a Bréguet 901 to victory at St. Yan, France, thus becoming the only American to win a World Soaring Championships.

**1961, Feb. 25** Paul Bikle establishes a world absolute altitude record of 46,267 ft. over the Rand Mts., near Lancaster, California, flying a Schweizer 1-23E.

**1964, July 31** First flight in excess of 1,000 km. (1,041 km.) by Alvin H. Parker, from Odessa, Texas, to Kimball, Nebraska, in a Sisu 1A sailplane.

tractive looking glider, but gained a certain amount of distinction when Heini Dittmar used it to set Germany's second two-place altitude record, 9,186 ft., in May of 1935.

The great interest in wave flying, generated in large part by the many notable flights in the Owens Valley in the early 1950's, led to a number of studies for stratospheric sailplanes. In these designs a low sink rate is highly to be desired, circling performance is of no great consequence, and ground-handling problems can generally be limited by the use of a single field for all take offs and landings. Large spans do not, consequently, create the same sort of troubles they do in gliders designed for general use and for thermal flying.

Most of the nations noted for gliding activities have produced at least one design study for a stratospheric sailplane. In France it was the Bréguet S-10 (span: 79.4 ft.) and in England a pressurized model by Slingsby having a span of 80 ft., 377 sq.ft. of area and a gross weight of 2,700 lbs. Concurrent with the Sierra Wave Project the Southern California Soaring Association developed two detailed studies for high-altitude sailplanes. The smaller of the two designs had a span of 100 ft., a gross weight of 3,250 lbs. and a calculated sink rate of 2.3 f.p.s. at 42 knots. The span of the larger design was 120 ft. With a lower relative gross weight of 3,700 lbs. it had a lower wing loading (6.2 against 7.2 lbs./sq.ft.) and a lower calculated rate of sink, 2.0 f.p.s. The SCSA study got as far as having a forward fuselage mock-up built, which is further than most such studies went.

It was World War II that spawned the really large gliders. At this point it is timely to note that there is an interrelationship between the linear, area and volumetric modes of aerial objects that makes larger machines more economical; put another way, the load than can be carried by a flying machine of given proportions will rise exponentially with any increase in wing span. Thus, when it came to the military requirements of transporting troops and supplies, the large glider came into its own. War, in any event, breeds monsters.

The Russians experimented with troop-carrying gliders as early as 1934 when a 13-passenger tailless machine with an 8,000-lb. gross weight was designed by the students of the Kharkow Aviation Institute. The Soviets undoubtedly developed many de-

Big gliders need big appointments. Crewman hooks up a mammoth.

signs during the war, and unquestionably, with their penchant for gigantic aircraft, many of these were larger than the Antonov A-7, with its span of 62 ft. 5 in., but it is the only example of which we have any record.

The largest of the many wartime gliders built in the U.S. was Jack Laister's CG-10A *Trojan Horse*. It had a span of 105 ft., was 67 ft. long and several cuts above the average transport glider. Its cantilever wing, rear-loading platform with clam-shell doors, and retractable nose gear reflected the designer's lifelong preoccupation with efficient aircraft. Gross weight was 31,000 lbs. of which 18,000 lbs. was useful load. The *Trojan Horse*, despite its great size, probably came closer than any of the other wartime gliders to being a sailplane.

The British produced their H-series gliders during World War II, *Hadrian* (actually the Waco CG-4A), *Hotspur, Hengist, Horsa* and *Hamilcar*. The largest of these, the *Hamilcar*, exceeded the *Trojan Horse* in span, with a tip-to-tip measurement of 110 ft. Length was 68 ft., empty weight 18,500 lbs. and payload 17,500 lbs. With its great size, and a wing loading of 21.7 lbs./sq.ft., the *Hamilcar* needed something the size of the four-engine Handley-Page *Halifax* to tow it. The *Hamilcar*, incidentally, was one of those gliders that eventually became a real airplane (see TURN-ABOUT) by the addition of a pair of 965-HP Bristol Mercury engines, a modification that permitted it to plow along under its own power at 100 m.p.h.

One eventuality that must have given many and many a pilot of the cargo gliders food for thought was the possible effect on his anatomy of having several tons of cargo roll over him if the glider, for some reason (and he could probably think of quite a number), came to a screeching halt. Fortunately a number of glider designers, including those who drew up the *Hamilcar*, were equally concerned. How this concern bore fruit, the following anecdote illustrates.

During the very first demonstration of its ability to lift *Tetrarchs*, a very large British tank it had been designed to carry, one *Hamilcar* approached a bit fast, overshot its landing area, and came slam-bang up against the end of a Nissen hut. The building effectively stopped the glider, but not the tank. The *Tetrarch*, crew and all, ploughed its way through the hut, taking out a series of transverse brick walls that divided it along its entire length. The pilot and co-pilot, securely strapped in their compartment atop the *Hamilcar*, were unhurt. So too, by great good fortune, was the tank crew. In fact, during a session on the gunnery range later in the day, they were able to demonstrate that the tank had come through its rough landing quite able to go into action.

The incident with the *Hamilcar*, because of a slight pilot error, had proven a good deal more than might have been the case otherwise. That such an error could occur under the ideal conditions of training points up the fact that landing a 15-ton glider in poor light on a field one had previously seen only on a map, and with poles strewn about, perhaps with a following wind and a scattering of small-arms fire to contend with as well, was the sort of mission most pilots were just as happy to see other pilots handle.

* * *

IT WAS THE GERMANS, whose victories in the Lowlands and on Crete goaded the Allies into their glider programs, who produced the largest glider the world has ever seen, or is ever likely to see. Not only was the *Gigant,* as the Messerschmitt Me.321 was called, the largest glider of all time, but one of the largest aircraft ever built as well. It had a wingspan of 181 ft., was 93 ft. 4 ins. long, had 3,230 sq.ft. of wing area and a payload of 22,000 kg.—some 24 tons!

The development of the *Gigant* began in 1940 when both the Messerschmitt and Junkers factories were given orders to produce gliders able to carry 200 fully equipped troops. Plans were prepared in short order and work on the initial production batch begun. The fuselage of the *Gigant* was a steel-tube structure covered with fabric. The tail surfaces, which had an unusually high aspect ratio, were of wood construction and strut braced. The wing, of course, presented the greatest problems, and Messerschmitt used everything in the structural armamentarium in designing it. Thus we find a high taper ratio, a strut-braced center section and cantilevered outer panels. The spar consisted of four spanwise steel tubes, forming a rectangle in cross section, interconnected with a girder structure. Ribs were of wood. The wing forward of the spar was covered with plywood; from the spar back, with fabric. A droppable undercarriage consisting of one set of Junkers 90 wheels behind and a set of Me.109 wheels in front was used for take off. Skids were fitted for landing.

At every stage of its career the *Gigant* presented gigantic problems, and none more troublesome than getting its immense bulk off the ground and into the air. For its take-off run it required almost 4,000 ft. of concrete runway, and for towing . . . well, there wasn't much around equal to the task. At first a Junkers 90 was used, but these were in short supply, so trios of towing aircraft (called Troika-Schlepp) were tried, first using sets of Me.110's, then He.111's. This system was both trouble-

The biggest towing rig in gliding history: The composite He.111Z takes off with an Me.321 "Gigant" in tow.

some and dangerous, however, so a special tug was developed, the He.111Z. It consisted of two standard He.111 twin-engine bombers joined via a special center section on which an additional engine was mounted. The results (see photo) was a five-engine aircraft with two fuselages.

The *Gigant* apparently handled well, but required tremendous power to fly. It was evidently for this reason that the cockpit, which originally accommodated a single pilot, was later expanded to include two. The hazards of landing the immense glider, particularly in combat, can readily be imagined. There were no dive brakes, but a 20-meter diameter ribbon chute was available. Quite possibly this was the first instance of a brake-chute being used on a glider.

It seems certain beyond any question that a highly instructive and illuminating book could be written concerning the flight and combat history of the *Gigant*. As it is, only the sketchiest details are available. Finished gliders were sent to France in the summer of 1941, then to the Eastern Front for the attack on Russia. Here they were credited with a good service record, but their awkwardness on the ground made them easy prey to Russian fighters.

Ultimately the *Gigant* was transformed into a powered aircraft by the addition of six Gnome-Rhone 14N radial engines and a ten-wheel undercarriage. The payload dropped to 130 troops, or equivalent, and gave a take-off weight ranging up to 110,000 lbs. The Me.323, as this version was known, was manufactured in quantity first at Leipheim and Obertraubling (1942) and later by the Zeppelin Werke. They saw service on a variety of fronts, including North Africa, but, unless heavily defended, proved pitifully easy targets.

## Cockpit Confrontations

ON SEPTEMBER 18, 1783, a duck, a sheep and cock were sent aloft in a hot-air balloon as a prelude to man-carrying experiments. Since that day there is scarcely an animal of any sort, from stowaway mice to Roscoe Turner's lion cub, that has not found itself airborne on one pretext or another.

Gliders, by their nature, are less well suited to animal cargo than most other types of aircraft, yet a very presentable menagerie could be assembled from the assorted fauna found at one time or another in the sailplane cockpit. For initial variety consider the caged carrier pigeons that were to have been issued to all pilots participating in the Internationals in Spain in 1952; the very unwelcome 12-in. lizard one soaring pilot found crawling up his leg after a take off in the desert; Prince Bira's flight to 14,000 ft. in a *Minimoa* with his Sealyham, *Tichiboo,* along for companionship; or Gus Briegleb's aerial encounter with the black widow spider.

The black widow made its appearance three-quarters of the way through a loop at 7,000 ft. over Big Bear Mt. in the vicinity of Arvin, California. The year was 1940, and Gus was putting one of his pre-war designs, the BG-7, through its paces. He was also 3½ hours through a 5-hour duration flight and just a little bit bored—which is why he started looping—when the spider appeared. It was just above his nose, hanging from the canopy frame.

For a brief instant Gus considered brushing away the spider with his hand, but immediately thought better of it. Meanwhile airspeed was building up past 100 m.p.h. and he was faced with the delicate task of completing the loop without overstressing the glider or the spider. The maneuver was scarcely completed before the black widow went back into hiding, this time behind the instrument panel.

Gus Briegleb

During the hour and a half that remained of his five-hour flight, Gus was on pins and needles. That evening he received a good deal of ribbing from his fellow pilots, for even in those days he was known as a man who, on occasion, might just exaggerate a little bit. That night Gus drempt of black widows. Early the next morning he determined to settle accounts. Armed with his bugle, an instrument he used when he felt his voice was inadequate, and with a sleepy witness to back him up, he gave the BG-7 instrument panel the same sort of treatment the walls of Jericho (see *Joshua* 6) received in olden times. For reasons best understood by black widows, this one came out to see what all the fuss was about. Gus was vindicated.

A story of quite another sort, reported in the February, 1960, edition of *Australian Gliding*, comes from the other side of the world. It concerns a hawk that, for reasons best known to hawks, attached itself to the Adelaide Soaring Club and, according to the account, "consistently flew in deliberate formation with the sailplanes." This practice went on for months, apparently to the satisfaction of all parties concerned.

As time went by the hawk became increasingly friendly and flew closer and closer to the thermalling gliders. In a few instances, as a matter of fact, the bird got so close that it bumped into gliders in flight. On one of these occasions—helped, perhaps, by the pilot trying to get as close as possible—the bird struck the wind screen of a Grunau Baby and *fell into the cockpit.* There was a moment of wild confusion before the pilot could hoist the bird overboard and regain control of the Grunau, but neither party was worse for the encounter.

Then there was the time, during the war, that Don Stevens took a dog along as co-pilot of a CG-4A and—but that's a story that will be told presently.

## Quotable Quotes

"MORE THAN TWO PAGES were given on 4th December (1909) to a Mr. Horace Vaughn to describe how he built a biplane 'hang' glider with a box tail. Having discovered that it flew more efficiently with the top tail plane and both vertical panels removed, he concluded by simple extrapolation that it would fly still better if the remaining tail plane was taken off too. After his next attempt to fly, he decided the wreckage was not worth rebuilding, and acquired a Wright-Clarke glider."

—*Sailplane & Glider*

## The Wind That Drives Men Mad

THE TERMS Foehn Wall and Foehn Gap are familiar to the majority of soaring pilots because of their association with wave flying. These terms get their names from the Foehn wind of the Swiss Alps, a name in turn derived from the Latin word for the south wind.

Because the first recorded wave flights in gliders were made in the Foehn-created winds in the lee of the Riesengebirge, near Hirschberg, Germany, and because Wolf Hirth publicized these flights well, even naming one of his gliders, the *Moazagotl,* after the cloud formed by the wave, Foehn and wave have become perpetually linked. It by no means follows that every wind that creates a wave cloud, with its Foehn Wall and Foehn Gap, is a

Foehn wind. Quite the opposite is the case, although the mechanics of compression and decompression that play such an important role in the creation of Foehn-type winds are also instrumental in the creation of waves and lenticular clouds.

Properly speaking the Foehn is a wind native to Switzerland and the adjacent Bavarian district of Germany. The term has become generic, however, and is now meant to encompass that family of winds of which the Sirocco (Italy), Zonda (Argentina), Chinook (Canada and the northern U.S.), Canterbury Northwester (New Zealand), Bohorok (Sumatra) and Santa Ana (Southern California) are all members.

In olden times it was thought that the Foehn which blew over the Alps into Switzerland originated in the Sahara Desert. This explanation, while it had the virtue of accounting for the characteristics of warmness and dryness of the wind, did not go very far in explaining the fact that numerous Foehn winds originate in cool or cold climates and that the Foehn itself occasionally blows into Switzerland from the north. These inconsistencies induced individuals with a more flexible outlook on life in general, and wind in particular, to look elsewhere for explanations.

About a hundred years ago the Viennese meteorologist Hann offered an explanation for the hot, dry nature of the Foehn that permitted the wind to blow from any direction it desired. According to Hann's analysis, the creation of the wind begins with a low-pressure area to the northwest of Switzerland that draws air first from the Swiss plateau, then from the Alpine valleys and mountains to the south, and finally from the lowlands on the far side of ranges. It is this trans-Alpine wind that becomes the Foehn.

In the first stage of its journey, the trip up the southern side of the Alps, the Foehn-to-be is cooled and forced to deposit the majority of its moisture on the slopes as it ascends. The mechanics which give the wind its unique character begin on the far side of the range when, during its precipitous descent, the air is compressed and heated.

Compression at this stage is not the obvious thing to look for, but then neither is the tendency of water in a stream to dip downward ahead of an object, and to reach its high point further downstream as it does. This seeming incongruity notwithstanding, the air is compressed in consequence of which it increases in temperature on the order of 5 to 5.5°C. per thousand feet. Thus, with the heat due to a fall of some 5,000 to 6,000 ft. added to the characteristic of dryness, the Foehn wind flashes into life.

There is a prelude, which may include some cold and raw gusts of wind, followed by a brief calm. Then the Foehn rushes down into the valleys, frequently at gale velocities, blasting everything in its path. In its onslaught it may snap trees, loosen masses of rock, blow the roofs off barns and even overturn automobiles. By means best known to itself, it bores tiny holes in window panes. Shutters are closed against it, and in areas where the Foehn blows regularly no windows at all are built in that side of the house from which the wind comes.

Being hot and dry, the Foehn quickly evaporates the water from whatever it touches. When it persists for periods as long as a week, as it may during the spring of the year, it sucks the moisture from everything it touches. Fresh leaves shrivel and drop from trees. The wood in walls and floors shrinks and cracks appear in furniture. Skin becomes dry and tempers sharpen.

Eventually flammable articles become so desiccated that fire becomes a serious hazard. For this reason *Foehnwachter* (fire guards) patrol Swiss villages and towns during windy periods to make certain that all fires, including those necessary for chores such as cooking, are extinguished. Despite such precautions the Foehn causes many fires. One Alphine village, Meiringen, has been burned to the ground three times during the Foehn.

There is a brighter side to the Foehn, however. It is reputed to be able to melt more snow in 24 hours than spring sunshine can in two weeks. For this reason the Swiss have given it the name *Schneefresser,* or Snow Eater. The same name is given to the Chinook, a wind that bears the same relationship to the U.S. Rockies that the Foehn does to the Swiss Alps.

The timely arrival of the Chinook has frequently meant the difference between life and death for large herds of livestock and vast numbers of wildlife due to its ability to expose forage. It is said to be able to lift a 10-in. snow cover overnight and scoop up all the water within its path as well. On one occasion (at Harve,

Montana) it was observed to raise the temperature by 30° in three minutes. In certain instances snow has been observed to pass directly into the form of vapor. A strong Chinook is reputed to remove ice from ponds in the same manner, without the intermediate stage of melting.

The warming effects of Foehn winds are not always so dramatic, but are no less beneficial in other respects. In certain areas of Switzerland they help ripen fruit; in others they permit farmers to raise corn and cultivate vineyards. The wind is responsible as well for the semi-tropical micro-climate of the northern shore of Lake Lucerne (the Swiss Riviera) where one finds fig trees, cyclamens and camillias growing. It also produces a remarkable degree of visibility and a particularly transparent atmosphere in which distant mountains appear to be quite close and everything is sharply defined.

The Foehn in its benevolent aspect is considerably less arresting than the Foehn-as-villain, however, and particularly when the victim is man himself, for the effects of the hot wind on the human temperament are no less critical than on an oaken plank. At its most benign the wind is liable to have an oppressiveness that leads to languor, irritability and headaches. At its worst, when it adds its own heat to already sultry temperaments, it begins to loose the bounds of reason and good judgment. Tempers with high flash points begin to ignite. Passions errupt. Lawlessness increases. Knives flash. Victims fall.

These are by no means imaginary consequences, for few imaginary consequences, with the exception of the notion of justice, find acceptance in the courts of law. The courts, we find, have long since taken account of the Foehn and its brother winds. In Gold Rush days such winds were recognized as extenuating circumstances in trials for murder and other deeds of violence. In Sicily, where crime sometimes seems to have the status of a very popular hobby, and in some of the Arab nations as well, a hot wind may be entered as a mitigating factor by the defense.

Nature, however, seeks balance in all things. Among more rational people, as for example the Bavarians, we find the effects of the wind anticipated and judgments made before the event, not *ex post facto*. In Munich it is not uncommon for individuals with more than ordinary responsibility to defer decisions that might be adversely affected by excessively hot weather to a later date. Thus a German judge would not risk a heavy judgment while his own temper was deranged by the oppressive heat of the Foehn, but would wait until, in a dispassionate frame of mind, he could make proper allowances for the hours of searing heat and scorching wind that had eroded the patience of the poor contrite devil now before him in the dock who, quite beside himself had snatched up the coal stoker and — well, and sentence mercifully.

## Vignettes from The Perilous and Poignant Past (No. 114)

THE TIME WAS the spring of the year 1922; the event, the first British gliding contest at Itford Hill. The protagonist is Mr. R. H. Stockton, Esq., the author, Alan E. Slater:

"When at last he got a proper launch, all went well until there was a crack and the rudder bar snapped in half. But he glided on and on until he touched down at the bottom, whereupon all the piano wires went 'ping, ping' and the loosened wing slid forwards and blocked his exit from the cockpit. But he extricated himself, pulled the wing back into position, and made the whole thing look intact again, for fear some Royal Aero Club official should come to inspect the wreckage and stop him flying it any more. This flight earned him a distance prize from Col. Bristow.

"The machine was repaired during the night and was about to be launched into the fierce wind next day when a Rolls Royce drove up and out came a gorgeous creature exlaiming: 'Rex *darling,* how *marvelous* to see you again.' But before all was ready once more for a launch, a sudden gust from one side turned the glider right over on top of the lady."

—*Sailplane and Gliding*

# 4

## The Colditz Cock

ON THE FIRST of January, 1944, a group with the properly deceptive name of HEAVY INDUSTRIES set to work on the construction of a glider to be called the *Colditz Cock*. By most standards the *Cock* was not much of a glider. The wing span was 33 ft., the area 160 sq.ft. and the empty weight 160 lbs. The glide ratio with two persons aboard was calculated to be 13 to 1.

The *Colditz Cock,* however, was a very special glider with a very special purpose, and HEAVY INDUSTRIES a very special bunch of chaps. They were British POW's who, at the time the project was undertaken, were incarcerated in Colditz Castle, a maximum security establishment deep in wartime Germany.

Colditz was reserved for officers who had already managed at least one escape from a prisoner-of-war camp. Consequently those within its walls could be considered to be among the most escape oriented of all groups then in captivity. They were also in a situation that demanded the utmost in imagination and ingenuity. The utmost in imagination in this case was a glider in which two prisoners, launched from the roof of the castle, would sail to ultimate freedom.

The *Cock* was constructed in an attic workshop measuring 7 ft. by 20 ft. which HEAVY INDUSTRIES partitioned and sealed for the purpose. Access to the work area was through a trapdoor. The security of the establishment was maintained by a gang of lookouts that eventually numbered 40.

The initial gathering and preparation of materials demonstrated the sort of POW industry and imagination to which veteran TV watchers have become so accustomed. Floorboards (which some said were spruce) provided wood for wing spars. Their length, 16 ft., 6 ins., incidentally, determined the span of the glider. Wood for ribs, bulkheads and struts also came from out of floor, or off the walls, or from wherever it happened to be. Cupboard hardware and the under parts of beds produced material for the metal fittings. Control cables were improvised from barbed wire and from telephone cable.

Material was cut down to size using implements such as a saw made from a phonograph spring. As befitted an aeronautical undertaking, a Bureau of Standards was established and a material testing program begun. Occasionally the primitive test apparatus yielded before the sample, but it was nonetheless determined that the floorboards-cum-wingspar wood had a modulus of rupture of 9,000 lbs./sq.in. Construction was with animal and casein glue that came from the outside, via the guards, in return for cigarettes. Covering consisted of bedsheets doped with milk boiled and applied hot. In about ten months the job was complete.

Launching a two-place glider from the roof of a castle would be a neat trick under the best of conditions. To do it from the roof of Colditz at night, surrounded by unsympathetic people, who also carried guns, and furthermore, to attempt to land in the River Mulde (the land areas nearby were heavily forested) would require very special preparations.

These were made. One section of the roof provided a semi-concealed 60-ft. run facing the prevailing wind. Here there was a ridge over which a long row of tables could be placed to serve as a runway. On this a four-wheel dolly, carrying the glider, would run. Launch power would be supplied by a great stone ballast weighing almost two tons that would be cast off the roof at the critical moment. This, attached to the *Cock* by a system of rope and pulleys, would give the glider an estimated launch speed of 30 m.p.h. The final requirement was for two very brave men.

This exciting (in prospect) launching, alas, never took place. By October of 1944 when the *Cock* was finished, the war was drawing to a close. Furthermore the Gestapo was growing increasingly less friendly toward escapees. So the glider roosted until April of the following year when the U.S. First Army liberated the area. Then, for the first time, it was brought out of its closet and assembled. So far as is known no attempt was ever made to fly the *Colditz Cock* and no one seems to have determined what ever became of it. It may still be in the attic of the castle for all anybody knows.

## Vignettes from The Perilous and Poignant Past (No. 47)

THE TIME WAS September, 1934; the place, Sutton Bank, site of the British National Championships. The protagonist is Seymour Whidborne, more popularly known as Whiddy, and the author, Philip Wills.

"There was a stiff westerly blowing up the cliff-face, so we strapped him into the nacelled Primary and gave him a good

strong bunjy launch over the edge. The machine shot forward, and Whiddy, startled by the acceleration, pulled hard back on the stick, with the result that by the time the aircraft hit the knife-edged updraught it was climbing at an angle of perhaps 30°. The upcurrent hit her with an almost audible 'woof!', and coming on top of his brisk launch, this quite upset the remainder of Whiddy's *sang-froid*. Desperately he yanked the stick right back into his stomach, the spellbound watchers saw the gawky Primary shoot up until it was practically standing on its tail, perhaps 25 yards out from the edge and the same distance above it. She faltered, plainly puzzled; then a wing dropped, the nose fell in a stalled turn until it was almost vertically down, she did a half-turn of a spin, but, in the terrific updraught, without losing much height, like a model suspended in a spinning tunnel. Then she picked up speed. Whiddy's stick-in-tum brought her out into level flight, but now facing straight back at us. She whistled over our heads and back over the landing field downwind; Whiddy put on a desperate vertical turn, the port wing just scraped the heather, and—plump, there was the aircraft, Whiddy and all, resting on exactly the spot he had left perhaps 15 seconds before . . ."

— *Sailplane and Gliding*

## ▸ Patent on Thermals

WERE YOU AWARE that way back in 1945 a U.S. patent (#2,371,629) was issued on an invention the purpose of which was the production of thermals? It went to Frederick W. Lee, then of Owings Mills, Md. The device, if such it could be called, consisted of a circular layer of asphalt (or pitch or bitumen) some 50 to 60 feet in diameter spread one foot below ground level. Beneath this there was a layer of soapstone or magnesite bricks, designed to serve as a heat-storing unit, and, lower still, one of an insulating material such as mineral wool or glass wool. This device was tested and, it is claimed, helped gliders soar.

In recent years a greatly expanded version of the asphalt disc has been considered not simply as a means of creating a single thermal, but of engendering an entire sea-breeze front. And at a very moderate cost too, as sea-breeze fronts go.

The proposal is based on tests made in Arizona which showed that an asphalt surface in full sunshine may reach a temperature of as much as 19°C above that of the normal surroundings. This observation provided the basis for a proposal that a large area of asphalt, located about 35 miles inland from a suitably large body of water, be used to induce a sea-breeze circulation which would result in the formation of clouds and the production of rain. It was determined that a single acre of asphalt could provide enough rainfall to make three acres of land arable. Of a variety of systems evaluated, including de-salting and transport by pipe-line or tank car, the sea-breeze system was judged the most economical. The cost of large-scale projects in countries such as Libya, Venezuela and Western Australia, where such artificially stimulated sea-breeze fronts could be used to irrigate tens of thousands of acres of land that is now arid, would be less than three million dollars.

(A point of interest, which again demonstrates that nothing is ever as simple as it seems on the surface, is that the texture of the asphalt layer is of primary importance for transferring the accumulated heat to the adjacent air. Therefore blacktop, because of its smoothness, would evidently be less effective than a properly textured asphalt surface.)

A still more recent development in thermal- and cloud-making machinery has been devised and built by a French meteorologist named Henri Dessens. Dessens' device is a superstove covering 3,200 square meters of area with 100 burners that generate 700,000 kilowatts of energy. Dessens has not only managed to make thermals, clouds and rain, but is said to have cooked up an occasional cu-nim as well.

## John J. Montgomery

JOHN J. MONTGOMERY (1858-1911) was certainly one of the most enigmatic figures in the history of aviation, and one of the most tragic as well. The most problematical point in Montgomery's life and career relates to the claim that, in 1883, he made successful glides at Otay Mesa near the Mexican border in Southern California. On the one hand it is difficult to attribute to a 25-year-old, working independently and with no predecessors but the birds on which to draw, successful flights, one exceeding 600 ft., such as are claimed. The long and persistent labors of Lilienthal, particularly the years that passed before he could make claims such as those made for Montgomery in his very first season of gliding, and with his very first glider, tends one to scepticism.

On the other hand, a sympathetic examination of young Montgomery's accomplishments tend one to give him the benefit of the doubt. From our point of view today, his 1883 glider is unquestionably primitive in the extreme, but when we consider that it was created whole at a time when the airplane simply did not exist, that it featured cambered flying surfaces and a hinged horizontal surface for longitudinal control, and that it was essentially modern in configuration, we are forced to attribute to the young inventor an original creation of the highest order and to allow that he may well have done all he claimed, perhaps even a bit more. Montgomery's later achievements also bear out this point of view.

Montgomery further proved his original turn of mind—and his exceptional maturity for a 25-year-old—by not rushing his glider to the top of the nearest promontory and leaping off with it, but by conducting a series of glide tests using ballast. When these proved successful the machine was taken to Wheeler Hill on Otay Mesa, and according to the testimony of the Montgomerys, successfully flown in the slope currents created by the ocean breeze. The glider is supposed to have had about 90 sq.ft. of area and to have weighed 38 lbs. If we accept these dimensions, and allow a bodyweight of 140 or 150 lbs. for Montgomery, who appears to have been a man of middle stature, there seems to be no practical reason for disallowing the alleged flight. A quarter of a century later, Montgomery recalled it thus:

*"There was a little run and a jump, and I found myself launched in the air. I proceeded against the wind, gliding downhill for a distance of six hundred feet. In the experience I was able to direct my course at will."*

Montgomery built two more gliders shortly after his initial successes at Otay Mesa. As is so common in such cases, the designer neglected to build on his earlier work with the consequence that neither of these later gliders flew. In the first of the two machines Montgomery experimented with a hinged and spring-loaded trailing edge as an aid to lateral stability, but at the same time abandoned the cambered airfoil. In the second, these hinged surfaces gave way to independently pivoted wing panels. At this point his discouragment with practical tests turned Montgomery to theoretical work in aerodynamics. This was somewhat unfortunate, for he seems all his life to have excelled at the former while making very little progress with the latter.

On May the 6th, 1896, Samuel Pierpont Langley, Secretary of the Smithsonian Institution, successfully flew a steam-powered model tandem monoplane from a houseboat on the Potomac River in Washington. This was one of the most convincing demonstrations of heavier-than-air flight that had ever been made, and it seems certain beyond almost any question that when Montgomery began experimenting with the tandem-wing configuration later the same year it was as a consequence of the publicity which followed Langley's exhibition.

Montgomery was now a resident at Santa Clara College in Northern California. Here, and at various nearby sites, notably Aptos, he conducted extensive tests with small tandem-wing model gliders varying in span from 3 ft. to 8 ft. Stability and control were, of course, the first problems facing anyone hoping to achieve successful flight, and these were the problems Montgomery now attacked. The thoroughness with which he solved them was in part due to his fortuitous choice of the tandem monoplane configuration and to the extensive period of testing and experimentation which lasted from 1896 to 1904.

By 1903 Montgomery felt confident enough of his progress to move on to full-scale aircraft, and in the fall of that year completed two tandem-wing monoplanes. One of these, subsequently named the *Santa Clara* and used in public demonstrations the next year, was taken to the Pinacarta Ranch between Watsonville and Mission San Juan Bautista in the summer of 1904 and put through an elaborate flight-test program. This was evidently quite successful, and Montgomery was now prepared to move on to the next stage—manned flight.

* * *

It was at this point that the inventor faced the problem that all the pioneer glider builders had eventually to contend with, launching. The solution was one of considerable daring and reflected the obvious confidence that Montgomery had in his machines. The glider was to be carried aloft by a balloon and released at will by the pilot. This was the heyday of the airship pilot Tom Baldwin who, during his earlier career as a parachutist, had used the balloon as a launch vehicle. Early in 1904, as a matter of fact, Montgomery entered into contract with Baldwin, certainly with the end in mind of using one of Baldwin's airships for launching, but this partnership ended acrimoniously and Montgomery looked elsewhere.

It was finally Fred Swanton, manager of the Santa Cruz Beach Cottage and Tent City Corporation, who agreed to provide the necessary hot-air balloons. Swanton used the balloons in parachuting demonstrations that were intended to attract customers to his concessions. A couple of young firebrands named Daniel Maloney (known professionally as "Professor Lascelles") and Frank Hamilton were Swanton's jumpers. Naturally these two men became prime candidates for the role of pilot, or 'rider' as Montgomery preferred to call it.

It should be borne in mind at this point that Montgomery's mastery of stability and control as it related to his tandem monoplanes was such that he could rig them to fly as steadily with a man aboard as with ballast attached, but that he could so adjust them as to be quite maneuverable if he so desired. It was his intention that the pilots should at first have only the most limited control and that the descents should be little more than somewhat glamourized parachute jumps; thus he thought of the pilots essentially as 'riders.' If what he wanted was riders, however, he should have picked less energetic specimens than "Professor Lascelles" and his companion, for they were much more eager to be pilots than riders and constantly importuned Montgomery to give them more control than was his wont.

It was on the morning of March 16, 1905, that the first aerial launches of the glider (now named the *Santa Clara*) took place. The locale chosen for the exhibition was Leonards' Ranch at Aptos, California. The rider-pilot was Daniel John Maloney. By 8:00 A.M. the hot-air balloon had been inflated and was ready for service. Twenty men held it in check while Maloney seated himself on the small saddle located on the lower longeron of the glider. Later, in an interview reprinted in the *New York World,* Montgomery described the subsequent action as follows:

*"The hot-air balloon carried the aeronaut to a height of 800 feet when the full-scale model was cut loose and descended in rapid circles until within a short distance of the ground.*

*"At this stage in the descent Mr. Maloney made use of my instructions and brought the model almost to a complete standstill, and the landing was made in an apple orchard without*

*mishap to the device or its passenger. In fact, scarcely a twig on the tree in which the model landed was broken."*

When the balloon canopy had been recovered and the *Santa Clara* retrieved from the apple tree, another flight was made:

*"Upon his second descent, I instructed Mr. Maloney how to obtain a successful sustained flight. But in so doing I cautioned him not to be carried away by enthusiasm at the sensation of floating at his own will through the air. My experiments had taught me the delightful sensation which accompanies such a flight through space; and I especially warned the aeronaut not to attempt too much on this occasion.*

*"Following my instructions, Mr. Maloney cut loose from the balloon at a height of nearly three thousand feet and glided to earth in long, sustained circles, and with a speed which varied at his direction, and made (his) landing lightly as a feather in a wheat field nearby.*

*"When I went out to meet the aeronaut, I felt that I could do anything with that machine; and I felt that I had accomplished the first step toward successful aerial navigation."*

The pilot was even more enthusiastic:

*"I went up as before . . . and got 3,000 ft. above the ground before I cut loose. For a few minutes I simply poised in the air and then flew around in different directions, circling, darting back and forth, up and down, as easily as an eagle could have done it. I was up in the air eighteen minutes and never had the least difficulty in gliding. I don't believe there is a single improvement that can be made in the machine. It is perfect. The problem of aerial navigation is solved."*

That he could combine the initial manned flight tests of a new glider with the initial training flights of new 'pilots,' that he managed this, furthermore, with daring launches thousands of feet above the ground, and that this enterprise was conducted without mishap, indicates the thoroughness and precision with which Montgomery had made his preparations. These flights, coming at

Daniel Maloney being hoisted aloft beneath a hot-air balloon in Montgomery's *Santa Clara* during an exhibition arranged at Santa Clara College for The League of the Cross Cadets.

Montgomery (above) astride the lower bamboo longeron of his *Santa Clara,* probably about April of 1905. The three movable bars by which the pilot steered the glider are plainly visible. Below: a powered version of Montgomery's design, probably the one built in 1911 by Captain Horace Wild, a nephew of Tom Baldwin. The Bates air-cooled engine reputedly gave a speed of 60 m.p.h.

the time they did, must certainly be considered as one of the most stunning of all aeronautical achievements and vividly demonstrate the character of Montgomery's singular abilities. They incline us, perhaps, to give more credence to the inventor's early exploits, and it was on the basis of this sort of performance we were inclined, in regard to his alleged flights in 1883, to extend him the benefit of the doubt.

The Montgomery tandem-wing gliders, although they did not represent a significant line of aeronautical development, nonetheless merit a brief description:

The two tandem wings were essentially identical. Each had a span of 24 ft. and a constant chord of 4 ft. 3 ins. They were set about a chord's width apart, in the same plane, and at the same angle of attack. The spars, of which there were two per wing, were of ash or oak and fitted, at their roots, into steel sockets where they were secured by steel pins and wing nuts. The ribs were of laminated spruce, ¼″ wide by 3/16″ deep. Rib spacing was five inches. The covering was a light rubberized silk or percale into which pockets were sewn to receive the ribs.

The tail surfaces were two large intersecting semi-circles, a configuration borrowed from earlier gliders. The frames were of light wood stayed by wires arranged like the spokes of a wheel and fabric covered. The tail set was so arranged that the horizontal surface could be raised or lowered, but the vertical surface was apparently intended only for directional stability, not for control.

The fuselage consisted of three parallel fore-and-aft longerons with uprights and a good deal of piano wire bracing. In at least one glider these members were of bamboo, but in the *Santa Clara* they appear to have been made of pine or spruce. The wings were attached to the upper longerons, as was the tail group, and the operator straddled the lower one. There were, to be sure, a great number of wires, some apparently copper, others steel, holding things together. The wings were liberally guyed and held in a downward bow which brought the tips some two feet below the level of the center section. Two weight figures are given, possibly referring to two different machines of the same design, but different construction. If we accept the heavier of the two, 43 lbs., and add 145 lbs. or so for the pilot, we can see that the 180 or so square feet of wing area were lightly loaded.

The control system of the tandem monoplane was novel and, as we shall shortly see, extremely effective. The pilot's feet rested on a transverse stirrup bar that could be depressed as desired. This seems to have provided basic power to a second set of bars about four feet in length that ran under the pilot's armpits and which, no doubt, helped him to keep his position in the simple open framework. These bars, in turn, seem to have had their respective ends attached to sets of wires that ran to the leading edges of the wings. Control of the horizontal tail surface was left to the hands. Clothesline running through pulleys served to actuate the surfaces.

As unorthodox as Montgomery's control system seems by modern standards, it was extremely effective. The pilot could bring the majority of his bodyweight to bear, with natural movements, on the flexible surfaces, depressing them alternately or in conjunction as desired.

* * *

THE CULMINATING POINT in the aeronautical career of John J. Montgomery was the demonstration arranged for the celebration of President's Day, April 29, 1905, at Santa Clara University. Although this was originally intended to honor the Reverend Robert Kenna and was planned for the entertainment of the university students and faculty, word quickly spread when the inflation of Frank Hamilton's hot-air balloon began and a throng of about 1,500 people assembled. Preparations were complete by late morning and Maloney and the glider were hoisted aloft to an altitude estimated at 4,000 ft. at which height the release was made.

A great deal of patently romantic nonsense has been written about Maloney's descent on April 29th and the most lurid accounts, as is so frequently the case, are the ones that have been most often repeated. The following is typical:

*"In the course of the descent the most extraordinary and complex maneuvers were accomplished—spiral and circling turns being executed with an ease and grace almost beyond description, level travel accomplished with the wind and against it, figure-eight evolutions performed without difficulty, and hair-raising dives were terminated by abrupt checking of the movement by changing the angles of the wing surfaces. At times the speed, as estimated by eye-witnesses, was over sixty-eight*

*miles an hour, and yet after a flight of approximately eight miles in twenty minutes the machine was brought to rest upon a previously designated spot, three-quarters of a mile from where the balloon had been released, so lightly that the aviator was not even jarred, despite the fact that he was compelled to land on his feet, not on a special alighting gear."*

What seems to be somewhat closer to the truth is that Maloney did maneuver the glider pretty much at will, that he made abrupt changes of direction and attitude and "headway against the wind," that he possibly achieved his own estimate of a speed of 25 m.p.h. and that he made a safe landing at a predetermined spot. This was spectacular enough in any case, and if anyone could normally be counted on to color it, a local newspaperman might. In the judgment of H. P. MacEnery of the *San Jose Mercury and Herald,* however, "the motions, counter-motions, and inter-motions that ensued, while not seemingly spectacular, were intensely interesting . . ."

Also intensely interesting, at least to soaring pilots, was a part of the flight that did not receive notice in the press, but appeared in a letter from Montgomery to Octave Chanute dated April 30th, 1905. "The day," Montgomery wrote, "was one of constantly changing light winds and when about 1,000 ft. high suddenly the wind seemed to be in all directions at once: and he thought he had struck a funnel of rising air and was carried up and seemed to drop, then rest almost motionless." It sounds as if Maloney, in addition to his other accomplishments, was the first glider pilot to encounter a thermal in free flight.

Even by today's standards the flight of the Montgomery glider, with its balloon launch, aerobatic flight and spot landing would be a spell-binder; we can readily imagine the sort of impression it made in the year 1905. Little wonder that Montgomery, his stock at an all-time high, was able to expand the scope of his operations, hire new riders and engage in a series of aerial exhibitions in other California cities. During one of these, at San Jose on May 21st, the proposed flight was aborted when Maloney discovered a general looseness in the airframe. The *Santa Clara* had been left unattended during the inflation of the launch balloon and, according to the post mortem, bolts had been tampered with, wires twisted and rods bent until a release "would have meant nothing less than a terrible fall to the ground, resulting in certain death." As on other occasions, Maloney stayed with the balloon until it descended at Gilroy, 30 miles distant.

It was an omen, for although Montgomery and Maloney had learned a lot in their brief partnership, they were not yet practiced in that tireless care which is essential to survival in the demanding medium of the air. Maloney's turn to pay for his insouciance came during a launch on July 18th, 1905, when a dangling balloon release cable fouled the tower which held the wires that braced the rear wing. Montgomery yelled to Maloney, directing him to ride the balloon down, but the warning was evidently lost in the cheers of the crowd.

Daniel John Maloney, Aeronaut

Shortly after release, the right rear wing of the glider folded upwards and Maloney's final descent began. It ended on a flat bit of ground near Eberhard's tannery, east of the Alameda, with the tanners as eyewitnesses. In the best aeronautical tradition, Maloney gave them a little farewell salute just before he hit. Maloney never regained consciousness following the impact. He died several hours later in the college infirmary. His career as a glider pilot had lasted just two days more than four months.

Maloney's death fell heavily on Montgomery, but it did not long impede his progress. The outset of 1906, as a matter of fact, found him as ambitious as ever. He was evidently contemplating the construction of a new type of glider better suited to soaring flight and was on the point of attempting a glider flight across the Santa Clara Valley from a point on the side of Mount Hamilton, near the Lick Observatory, 4,000 ft. above sea level. According to one record, he had at this time 16 inscriptions for gliding instruction, each of which presumably entailed the sale of a glider.

In effect the scene was set for the true birth of soaring flight on a regular and consistent basis. Montgomery had everything necessary; an airworthy glider, able pilots, a cadre of enthusiasts, an excellent soaring site, adequate financing and shop facilities and a thorough understanding of what was required. It is probably risking very little to claim that within a year or two at the most, Montgomery would have established soaring as a practical reality. An Act of God intervened, however, the San Francisco Earthquake of April 18th, 1906. It did little damage to Montgomery's workshop, but did create a general economic depression which made it quite impractical to continue with aeronautical experiments on the scale previously contemplated.

Although Montgomery did not get back to flying for a number of years, there seems to have been no serious break in his activities. It was in 1907, by his own later guess, that Cornclius Reinhardt, a skilled German mechanic, went to work for Montgomery in his workshop at Santa Clara College. Details are scarce as regards Montgomery's activities for the next few years, but early in 1910 he married and in October of 1911, at the age of 53, he began his third and last series of aeronautical experiments.

Montgomery's final fling at flying took place at the Ramonda Ranch, a locale southeast of San Jose, California. Here there was an ideal natural site named Horseshoe Hill. In this instance the open section of the horseshoe faced southwest toward a stretch of flat country and the distant San Jose Mountains. The sides of the horseshoe were low hills; the remaining side provided a somewhat steeper slope. It was here, dropping into the flat valley that spread out below, that a set of wooden rails were laid for launching.

Montgomery, his wife, the aforementioned Cornelius Reinhardt, and another collaborator, Joseph Vierra, established camp at the base of Horseshoe Hill on October 17th and spent the next fortnight conducting tests. During this period Montgomery and Vierra, as pilots, logged 54 or 55 successful flights in Montgomery's latest glider, *The Evergreen.* The best description we have of these flights is that supplied a half century later by Reinhardt. He claimed they included gliding, rising, maneuvering and circling in the breeze back to the hilltop.

If Reinhardt's attestations are substantially true, it seems

Forward fuselage area of a reconstruction of Montgomery's 1911 monoplane with clear details of seat and modern control wheel.

quite probable that Montgomery established some world gliding records on this occasion, possibly even exceeding the 9 min. 45 sec. duration record established by Orville Wright earlier that same month at Kitty Hawk. If Reinhardt is correct, Montgomery made significant headway in the art of soaring flight and brought the technique of slope soaring to a level of development that would not be matched until the heyday of the German pilots on the Wasserkuppe a decade later. Such, however, was the nature of fate, that Montgomery was to receive scant credit for these final accomplishments.

Montgomery's new glider, his sixth design, was a 26-ft. monoplane of conventional configuration. The fuselage was an open framework of four bamboo longerons. These joined at the back in a more or less conventional tail. The fin was evidently a fixed surface not used for steering. The stabilizer was a large lifting surface, something of a throwback to the tandem monoplane design. It could be set at any desired angle, within limits, but was not used for control while in the air. The pilot sat on a rocker seat of the Deperdussin type and was equipped with a pair of handsticks (later changed to a yoke and wheel). With the exception of the bamboo longerons, most of the structure of the fuselage, the cross members and uprights, were made of metal and held together with stove bolts, Four 14-in. baby carriage wheels with solid rubber tires served as landing gear.

The wing of the new glider was its most remarkable feature. With its single surface and downward bow at the tips it had a superficial resemblance to the wings of the tandem monoplanes, but in reality it was a good deal more complex. It has to be, for the entire control of the glider was achieved through manipulations of the wing. Banking and turning were effected by warping down the trailing edges of the outer wing panels and the angle of incidence of the central panel of the wing could be varied as much as five degrees for longitudinal control. All the wing ribs fitted into sleeves sewn in the fabric, as did the rear spar. The ribs in their turn were secured to the front spar by swivel clips. What stiffness the surface had, beyond what little the structure itself provided, was supplied by Montgomery's use of the stressed-skin technique in the wing covering, one of its earliest applications.

With this new machine Montgomery once again seemed to be on the brink of success. Once again, however, fate intervened. During an otherwise normal flight on the last day of the encampment, October 31st, Montgomery stalled shortly after take off. The height was not great, 13 ft. according to Reinhardt, 23 as Vierra reckoned it. But Montgomery could not regain control, and the glider slipped to the side, struck its right wingtip, and overturned.

The damage to the glider, which was photographed shortly

*The Evergreen* begins a take-off roll down Horseshoe Hill.

after the accident, was minor, indicating that the fall was not a bad one. As ill luck would have it, however, Montgomery was thrown to the right, and when the glider hit, his head struck the juncture of the upper right longeron and the forward upright. When it did so, a protruding stove bolt penetrated his skull just behind the right ear. It was two hours before the doctor, who was summoned immediately by telephone, arrived. By then Montgomery was dead.

It was such an inconsequential thing, so trivial as flying accidents go, yet how perfectly it fit into the perverse pattern of Montgomery's life, how fittingly it finally punctuated the last sentence in a career of tantalizing successes and—always—the heavy hand of some greater and sterner power.

## Vignettes from The Perilous and Poignant Past (No. 33)

THE TIME WAS July 14, 1932; the place, South Mountain, Elmira, New York, during the third U. S. National Soaring Championships. The protagonists,

"Joseph Funk and Frank Gross, both of Akron, flew their two-place machine for more than four hours, Gross dangling his legs over the side of the cockpit to relieve his cramped position.

In the midst of their cruising, they remembered that they had left some potatoes boiling on their camp fire. They were living in a little camp on the mountain. In the excitement of getting off when the wind unexpectedly arose, they forgot the spuds. So they circled low over the ridge and shouted requests for investigation of the status of the potatoes. Spectators rushed to the camp fire and found the potatoes badly burned. Gross and Funk kept on flying."

—*The Gliding and Soaring Bulletin*

## Looping the Loop

ONE OF THE FADS of the 1930's, along with marathon dancing and flagpole sitting, was looping the loop. It was a pastime pursued by all sorts of pilots in all sorts of aircraft, gliders included. Because of their limitations, gliders could not hope to compete with records such as the 1433 consecutive loops that the late "Speed" Holman performed above the St. Paul Airport during a five-hour session back in 1928. They did, nonetheless, turn away in their own corner of the sky and set their own unique records.

In September of 1933 the U.S. glider looping record, held by Russ Holderman of Leroy, New Jersey, stood at a modest 35. A number of people, including Jack O'Meara, who had done 43 loops in practice, were out to beat this record, and at the Akron, Ohio, glider meet, October 14-15, 1933, two pilots did. One was Bud Sutherland, who did 63 loops, the other Willis Sperry, who managed 68. Both pilots had begun with tows to 10,000 ft.

Activity on the glider looping front was quiet for a few years until Don Stevens showed up on the scene. Gliders are different things to different people. To Don the glider was a plaything that came along just in time for him to have plenty of fun, and he seldom let an opportunity pass.

One such opportunity was the National Soaring Championships held at Elmira, New York, in 1936. During this event Stevens was towed to an altitude of 11,000 ft.—9,000 ft. above the ground—where he released and began looping. As it chanced, Don encountered a thermal after his first 54 loops which permitted him to do the next 13 without any appreciable loss of height. Twenty more followed hard on these and another five were thrown in at random before landing. The ground-to-ground time of this flight was one hour; the portion during which the 92 loops were done occupied 22 minutes and the average height loss per loop was 100 feet.

Don Stevens was not the world's looping champion by any means, but we have a special interest in him which will be evident shortly. Meantime we can turn our attention to RAF Flight-Lieutenant E. L. Mole, who, unaware of Stevens' 92 loops, not to mention the 125 that Wolf Hirth had done even earlier, had himself towed to 8,000 ft. over the airfield at Cairo, Egypt, and turned 67. That was in 1937.

The next year, armed with the knowledge that others had gone before him and done better, Mole was back at it. This time, in place of the relatively primitive *Wolf* in which he had done his 1937 stint, he had a Hungarian M-22, a sailplane so modern that it had aileron-linked full-span flaps. And, instead of a mere 8,000, he now towed to 15,400 ft. Looping begain immediately and continued until 147 had been accomplished. In relating the account, the pilot had this to say:

*"There is no doubt that giddiness whilst looping is accentuated by high altitude, and I found that after a while I was unable to read the instruments. Later I was unable to find the aerodrome and landed two miles away in the desert. On stepping out of the glider I fell straight over backwards."*

Now back to Don Stevens. When he went to war, as he did not many years after his Elmira exploit, it was, characteristically, as a glider pilot. And nothing would do but that, once he had access to a Waco CG-4A, which he did when he arrived in North Africa, he should resume looping where he left it off as a civilian. The size of the big Waco (span: 83 ft. 8 ins.; gross weight 9,000 lbs.) might have discouraged anybody else, but to Don, the eternal showman, it simply presented an excellent opportunity to take some friends along on the caper. Here is the way it was told on Don Stevens' Page in *Soaring* magazine:

*"Flt. O. Stevens, accompanied by 2nd Lt. Wilbur A. Brown as co-pilot, Flt. O. Earl H. Jarrett and 1st Lt. William N. Schneider as passengers, set out on an altitude test flight. In*

*the tow plane were 1st Lt. Donald E. Sanders and 1st Lt. Jack L. Saulsbury.*

*"At an altitude of 12,500 feet, the glider cut loose from the tow plane and immediately pulled up into a loop, since loss of altitude was then desired. Flying conditions were not ideal, because the 25 MPH wind tended to force the glider away from the base during the descent and it was necessary for the pilots to check their position frequently. The passengers in the glider kept a count of the number of loops by marking them on a sheet of paper during the descent. Flt. O. Jarrett, equipped with a camera, had a time trying to take photos as they were looping. Special rigging was necessary to hold him down while he took action photos of the loops.*

*"Thirty-one consecutive loops were executed before the wind had forced them sufficiently far away from the base to necessitate a change in position. Flt. O. Stevens turned the glider and started looping toward the field and executed an additional 15 loops. At 3,500 feet, Flt. O. Stevens again checked his position. He turned toward the field again, again nosed her down, and continued looping. As the glider looped, right wing heavy, it was difficult to loop in the direction they wanted to. Eight more loops were completed, the final one being executed off the end of the runway into a strong wind, at an altitude of 100 feet. As the glider hung on its back, a bare 100 ft. off the ground, one of the passengers exclaimed: 'I sure hope she goes*

*on over, 'cause if she doesn't—.' By the time we were around and we leveled off, the wheels touched for a landing.*

*"Constant pull of centrifugal force and the tugging of the safety belt exert a terrific strain on physical reserve and the pilots and passengers of the glider expressed fatigue upon landing. A total of 54 inside loops were completed during the descent. Taking 12 minutes of continuous looping, the pilots claim that under favorable conditions 75 to 80 loops could be made easily."*

It is not difficult to read between the lines, and to imagine that the narrator of the above passage was not above the use of euphemism when he described the looping party as "expressing extreme fatigue." In any event the next communication concerning looping is from Flt. O. Stevens himself. Apparently he has been unable to cajole any more of his fellow officers into another flight:

*"I made a solo flight today in the Big Job and took a dog with me as co-pilot. I sat him down in the seat and showed him how he could stick his nose out the window. We took off, the dog and I, and circled the field—the dog thought it was great stuff and really enjoyed it. I cut loose at the end of the runway at 1000 feet and dove to 150 M.P.H. The dog held on all fours to keep from sliding off the seat. As I leveled a bare 25 ft. off the ground, I pulled into a loop. I looked over at the dog and the G-force had spreadeagled his two front paws and his jaw, as well as his big ears, were flat on the seat. On the top of the loop the dog, ears and four feet, left the seat and he was resting on top of the windshield upside down (had 400 ft. on top of the loop and 60 M.P.H.). As I came on around and leveled off for a landing, the dog flew back to the seat, spreadeagled, his eyes as big as dollars. As I landed and stopped, the dog jumped off the seat, made a bee-line for the door and when I opened it, dashed out. I tried later to get him into a glider, but he had had enough—no dice!"*

In answer to the logical question, no, Flight Officer Stevens wasn't. He survived the war and at least a score of postwar years of varied activity.

# 5

## Early Russian Progress

NOT ONLY DID THE GERMANS have a substantial head start on the rest of the gliding world in the years between World Wars I and II, but they had some excellent press agents in the persons of men like Wolf Hirth and Robert Kronfeld. Although the Russians did not begin gliding seriously until the middle 1920's, and despite the fact that their early endeavors were overshadowed by activities on the Wasserkuppe, they approached the new sport with tremendous enthusiasm and energy; a decade of intense activity brought them, in many respects, to a level of achievement that compared very favorably with that reached by the Germans. They never did have anywhere near the success of the Germans in making their exploits known to the world at large, however, but enough details exist to show what an industrious and accomplished lot the Soviet pilots were.

By 1935, the year of the eleventh All-Soviet Glider Meet at Koktebel, in the Crimea, the Russians were in full swing and entering a period of the most intense and fruitful activity. They possessed, at this early date, a cargo glider with an 18-passenger capacity; they were busy making a remarkable series of extended towed flights, some as long as 1000 miles; and they were constantly breaking new ground, particularly in the matter of long-distance soaring flights.

The immortals of early Russian gliding, Kartashev, Rastorguyev, Iltchenko and Klepikova, repeatedly established new records, leap-frogging each other up the mileage scale. Kartashev, then an instructor at the Moscow Gliding School, began matters

This multiple tow of 11 gliders, probably photographed about the year 1940, is representative of the sort of activity common in Soviet gliding in the period between World Wars I and II.

in style during the summer of 1935 with a flight of 106 miles in a G-9 glider. The details of the flight are more impressive than the distance. It was made on a storm front that Kartashev contacted at nine o'clock in the evening and stayed with till 1:30 A.M.

Kartashev made a giant's step forward the following year, almost tripling his previous distance. This flight, made on September 1, 1936, carried him 501.2 kms. (313.75 mi.) and was only 3 kms. short of the world distance record that had been established in July of the previous year by the famous Brno quartet, Rudolph Oeltschner, Otto Braeutigam, Hans Heinemann and Ernst Steinhoff. Two weeks later, on the 14th of the month, Kartashev set out in his GN-7 and this time flew 331.25 miles. Although this exceeded the existing mark by an adequate margin to qualify as a new world record, it was not so entered.

The monopoly of Kartashev was broken the following year by Victor Rastorguyev who, in the month of May, made three notable long-distance flights from Moscow. The last of these, on the 27th, ended in the village of Jarygenskaya, 404 miles from Moscow. On the same day Iltchenko established a two-place world distance record of 253 miles flying a KIM-3 *Stanhonovetz*. Kartashev eclipsed this on July 22nd of the following year with a 400-mile flight. Iltchenko, incidentally, got the two-place world distance record back with a 515-mile flight in an A-10 sailplane in May of 1953.

The culmination of the Russian pre-war endeavors was an epochal flight, on July 6, 1939, of 749 kms. (465 mi.) by Olga Klepikova, a distance mark that was to stand for 22 years. It is, of course, well known that some of these Russian distance flights, but by no means all, were made with the help of very high starts (see TOWS TO THE STRATOSPHERE) and others were assisted en route by giant bonfires. Today we have the altitude penalty, not to mention the vigilance of Smokey the Bear, and such tactics are out of the question. At the time they were quite legitimate, however, even pioneering.

## Vignettes of the Perilous and Poignant Present (No. 1)

THE TIME was not so long ago; the locale, certain airfields strewn about Southern California. The protagonists are two brothers named Jessop.

"Karl and Dave happily took off from Orange County Airport in Dave's 172 and headed for Tehachapi (110 miles) where they were going to take delivery on Karl's new 2-33. They arrived, took possession of the ship, and made preparations to head home. After the pre-flight check, and amid happy good-byes, they saddled up for the long tow home, Karl comfortable on his donut air cushion in the glider, Dave in the Cessna.

"Came the take off and Karl was just wobbling down the runway when bedlam broke loose. It sounded as if the brand new glider was falling apart! Was the wheel gone? Was a strut dragging? Karl didn't look, he just released and pulled off the runway. After his heart got back in place he climbed out to survey the wreckage, just as everybody rushed up. Look they did, and all they found was . . . nothing. It seems the rear window was not secured before take off and had started banging against the wing. With a few choice words Karl locked and taped the window latch and saddled up again.

"But now where was brother Dave? Nobody had told him about the release and by this time he was a speck on the horizon, doing a masterful job of pulling the tow rope to Elsinore, 125 miles away. After he recovered, Karl placed a call to Florence Perkins at Skylark and asked her to break the news to Dave when he arrived. This he did after two hours of flying at 60 m.p.h. After landing he rolled up to the gas pump, got out of the ship and scanned the sky for Karl with that 'Now what the h---'s he up to?' expression on his face. At this point Florence walked up, grinning, gave him the jolt, and broke up completely as Dave gasped and staggered backward against the Cessna, muttering the sort of remarks generally reserved for smashed fingers and barked shins.

"But it was too late to go back for Karl, so Dave flew the Cessna back to Orange County Airport and tied down. Meanwhile, back at Tehachapi, Karl had calmed down enough to take a tow to 2,000 ft. He found a good thermal and was soon at 10,000 ft. Might as well head for home without the towplane, he figured. After all, it *had* been done. Then he would really have brother Dave, but good. But Karl ran out of day near El Mirage, so put in there for the night. He also placed some calls for Dave, who by this time was on the job taking care of his air conditioner business.

"So dawned a new day and Dave lit out as soon as he could and flew back to Tehachapi. When they told him where Karl was his hat really hit the ground, so hard the boys at 4,000 ft. felt it. So it was back in the Cessna where he firewalled everything and got the STOL out of there for the 60-mile trip to El Mirage. Brother Karl was looking in the wrong direction when Dave landed and didn't see him come in.

"So the brothers were united, and after they stopped yelling at each other Karl settled on his donut ready to go again. But did the Brothers Jessop hook up and go peacefully fading off into the sky? Was this the end of their problems? Not quite yet. Karl was all set, but Dave was out there jumping up and down. He didn't have *time* to make the long tow. He had to get back on the job. His customers were sweating.

"So Karl climbed wearily out of the 2-33 and into the Cessna and it was full bore back to Orange County (75 miles). Dave headed for work while Karl flew over to Skylark (35 miles) and picked up Ray Brown, a *real* tow pilot. Then back to El Mirage (75 miles) where—after carefully adjusting the rear-view mirror—they towed off to Skylark. This adds up to 730 air miles of flying to get the 2-33 moved 110 miles and qualifies the Brothers Jessop for the Royal Order of the Cast Iron Tow Rope."

—*Zero Sink*

## Goal Flight in a CG-4A

DURING WORLD WAR II vast numbers—perhaps as many as 30,000, perhaps more—gliders of various sizes and shapes were built for the purpose of transporting men and materiel to combat areas. Inevitably a certain number of these gliders found their way into the hands of experienced soaring pilots and inevitably one or another of these pilots found himself presented with the opportunity to engage in his favorite sport. From the many surviving accounts of troop gliders being deliberately soared, and not only for fun, but for badges as well, it seems fair to assume that most of these opportunities were very small and grew by degrees. Such, at least on the face of it, does not seem to have been the case with Chester Decker and the CG-4A.

During World War II Decker was engaged in flight training work using the Waco CG-4A, an 84-ft. span glider with a gross weight of 9,000 lbs. He was well suited for the work, having been the U.S. national soaring champion in 1936 and 1939. The episode in question began over the state of Ohio, at an altitude of about 7,000 ft., on one of those days ideally suited to soaring, but not necessarily to towing. Not only was the air turbulent, but the Waco, with ten fully loaded soldiers in the back, became increasingly unwieldy. With fifty miles yet to go the tow line parted, leaving the glider and its occupants stranded in mid-air.

Under ordinary circumstances a forced landing would have followed. With a glider such as the Waco this was certain to entail a costly retrieve even without such eventualities as crop or property damage occurring. Decker, of course, did what any red-

blooded ex-National Soaring Champion would have done given the occasion: he began flying to his destination. This approach to the matter caused some discontent among the troops who doubted that the careening glider was under intelligent control. Decker was not the sort to let ten armed men stand in his way, however. And they were of a different turn of mind when the pilot, only an hour behind schedule, landed the glider safely at its destination. Then he was a hero.

## A Tibetan Glider

IN HIS AUTOBIOGRAPHICAL book, *The Third Eye,* the Tibetan Lama, Tuesday Lobsang Rampa, tells of the age-old popularity of kite flying in his native land and of his own considerable experiences piloting man-carrying kites. He also tells the story of the flight of an untethered kite which, if true, should certainly be added to the lore of early gliding.

Many years ago, as a boy, Rampa visited the lamasery of Tra Yerpa, high in the Himalayas, where the art of kite flying was far advanced. The young acolyte was small even for a nine-year-old and his precocity was exceeded only by his eagerness to fly in one of the lamasery's kites. This he shortly did. His enthusiasm waxed ever keener and soon he was offering suggestions designed to increase the maneuverability of the kites.

Rampa's ideas were obviously tending in the direction of free flight, and it was in this connection that the portly Master of the Kites, whose respect the young pilot quickly gained, told him how, "many years ago," an untethered kite resembling an elongated bird, and bearing a man, had been launched from a nearby ledge and had flown some 20 miles before it hit the side of a mountain. The reader, of course, is free to believe this or not, as he chooses, but the absence of a modern Tibetan air force would seem to bear the story out.

## Turnabout

THERE HAS ALWAYS been a certain amount of give and take between the respective lines of development of powered and unpowered aircraft. That most of the give has been from the glider side is well documented in an article entitled *Contributions of Gliding and Soaring to Aviation* (*Soaring* for March-April, 1945) in which Wolfgang Klemperer outlines half a hundred or so instances of pioneering work done in gliders that was subsequently adopted by general aviation. Klemperer's impressive list includes the prone pilot position, variable-incidence wings, high aspect ratio surfaces, D-type hollow monospars and a good deal more. As we shall presently see, the process is still going on.

Two instances of turnabout. Above, a C-47 turned into an XCG-17 by removing the engines and adding two aluminum hemispheres. A second C-47 was used for towing. The Taylorcraft TG-6 (opposite) was typical of the conversions made by lightplane manufacturers when quantities of training gliders were needed in a hurry.

The two lines of development, of course, began as one, for it will be remembered that all the great trail blazers, from Cayley to the Wrights, either added engines to their gliders or contemplated doing so. When it was demonstrated that powered flight was possible, the proponents of the airplane took possession of one half of the primal aeronautical equation and occupied themselves with adding power to retrograde airframes while the other half fell, almost by default, to the devotees of motorless flight who soon came to realize that progress in powerless flying machines was directly linked to the reduction of drag.

Eventually the two currents, or, more properly, some tributaries, moved back near enough one another for there to be some profitable exchanges. Perhaps no better examples could be found than in the work of Willi Messerschmitt and Alexander Lippisch, neither of whom seemed to have forgotten a whit of their early experiences with gliders when it came time to design what

was quite possibly the finest operational fighter of World War II and the world's first rocket-powered attack aircraft. The Me.109 derived a good share of its performance from its high aspect ratio wing and generally clean exterior. The stubby little Me.163 was reputed to have an L/D max of 20, a very high figure for the time and one achieved with an aspect ratio of only 4.5!

Occasionally, although not too often, the give and take between powered and non-powered aircraft goes beyond the simple exchange of ideas or isolated techniques and entire aircraft change hands. The instances in which powerplants have been added to gliders, or a propeller removed from a lightplane, and a tow release bolted on so that the ship could be used as a glider, are far from rare. World War II produced some notable instances of turn-about, the tide going one way at the outset and the other way at the conclusion. When training gliders were urgently needed in the early years of the war they were hastily improvised from standard airframes by Aeronca, Taylorcraft and others. Even the DC-3, with aluminum hemispheres covering

Turnabout during the war worked both ways as the modifications to this Waco CG-4A show. The addition of a pair of 175-h.p. Ranger engines turned it into the XPG (Experimental Powered Glider)-1. Another notable conversion was the Chase XCG-14A which, with engines added, had a successful postwar career as the *Aviatruk*.

empty engine mounts, became a temporary glider. When the time ultimately came to beat swords into plowshares gliders such as the Chase (U.S.) and General Hamilcar (Great Britian) were fitted with engines and became transport aircraft.

While the instances of powered aircraft being pressed into service for significant stints of gliding and soaring are rare, they nonetheless add an element of color without which the history of the sport would be notably poorer. From the available instances let us chose three, each made in an aircraft in no way modified for gliding. Our unusual trio consists of an ancient Hanriot biplane, a converted World War II fighter and a spy-in-the-sky plane in serious trouble. Together the three flights, one each duration, altitude and distance, would provide the qualifications for an off-beat sort of Gold badge—provided we overlook a technicality or two.

The duration flight was made by a soaring pioneer whose name is largely forgotten these days, the French Lieutenant Thoret. Part of the reason for Thoret's obscurity may be due to the unorthodox methods he used, for most of his soaring flights were made in unreconstructed powered aircraft. There was some precedent for this approach among the French, particularly in cases such as the successful thermal soaring flights made by Sergeant Aimé Grasset in a Dorand-Anzani biplane in July of 1914, but the rest of the world paid little attention.

Thoret's exploits as a duration pilot began with a flight of 7 hrs. 3 mins. on the third of January, 1923. This more than doubled the record of 3 hrs. 21 mins. established by Maneyrol in a Peyret tandem monoplane at Itford Hill the previous September. Thoret's mount was a Hanriot, a biplane typical of the epoch, flown with the engine stopped. The site was the French soaring camp at Biskra, Algeria. Although the flight constituted an honest world record it was not homologated nor entered as such. In any event it was promptly exceeded by Maneyrol in his Peyret (8 hrs. 5 mins.) and by Barbot in a Dewoitine glider (8 hrs. 36 mins.).

It was the Germans, of course, who first demonstrated the practicability of duration flying and who raised the world record to the three-hour level. The successful endeavors of the French were a challenge to at least one German, the intrepid Ferdinand Schulz, who responded to Barbot's record with a flight of 8 hrs. 42 mins. This began a 30-year seesaw contest between the French and the Germans which was intruded on by only two other nationalities—Massaux of Belgium and Lt. Cocke of the U.S.A. —and which ultimately drove the duration record past 56 hrs.

It was early in 1925 that Thoret, to get back to him, established a training operation at St. Remy-de-Provence that may well qualify as the first ever to successfully put the powered sailplane philosophy into effect. Thoret now used a cumbersome double-bay Hanriot for both instruction and solo flights. He himself made a soaring flight in excess of nine hours in the ship (the one we select to qualify for the duration leg of the Gold badge) and two of his students, the Sergeants Antoine and Wernert, both made flights of about nine hours. Later the same year, in September, Thoret was to be found on the northernmost tip of Corsica, just opposite Bastia, where he staked out a 40-kilometer course along the low hills of the island. Here he succeeded in flying for more than three hours. This time his Hanriot was equipped with floats for extra drag production and weighed in at one ton. Later still Thoret explored soaring over the Alps where he made some flights in a large single-engine monoplane carrying as many as a dozen passengers!

So much for duration.

Next item, a 14,000-ft. climb in a P-38, both engines stopped, both props feathered. It was an F-38 in reality, a P-38 modified for meteorological research. The pilot was Bob Symons and the locale Bishop, California, the home of one of the world's most phenomenal waves. Symons is credited with discovering the Bishop Wave in 1929 and claimed to have made more than 300 flights in it.

On his return to Bishop from a seeding run one day in 1951, Symons found the airport covered with clouds of dust; presumably the rotor that accompanies the wave was in full blast directly over the field. Symons realized that it would be a while before he could land and that it would be necessary therefore to conserve fuel. With the wave working, however, this presented no problem. Symons accordingly shut down one engine and feathered the prop.

Despite the cutback in power the '38 kept gaining altitude quite handily, so Symons stopped the other engine and feathered the other prop. He soared the airplane in this configuration for an hour, climbing to 30,000 feet in strong lift. It was probably only the extreme cold, and anxiety about starting the engines that caused Symons to stop at such a modest figure, for the wave was unquestionably in top form that day and could probably have carried him a good deal higher.

Anyhow, there's altitude.

Thus far we have two conditions for our aberrant badge. Now we must supply the distance element, and who, you are wondering, managed to soar the requisite distance in anything other than a glider? Well, so far as we know, no one. The instance we have in mind was not a soaring, but a gliding flight, and unlike the two other cases cited, quite an involuntary experience.

The victim-cum-hero of this episode was a U-2 pilot of the pre-Gary Powers epoch who suffered a flame-out while flying over the Atlantic Ocean several hundred miles from the nearest land. That land, as it chanced, was Bermuda, as a consequence of which the engineless pilot immediately radioed a *Mayday* to Kindley AFB requesting a radar fix. With this, and the feeling that he had sufficient altitude (80,000 ft.) to reach his destination, the pilot began what must have been one of the most exciting landing approaches in the history of aviation.

According to published accounts the U-2 reached Kindley about 40 minutes after the engine failure. A few rough calculations indicate that the average glide speed must have been on the order of 450 m.p.h., the rate of descent 2,000 f.p.m. and the glide angle just a shade under 20 to 1. The distance: 300 miles, half again the Gold badge requirement.

## ▸ Variometer Vagaries

THE VARIOMETER is without doubt the most important instrument on the panel of the modern sailplane and there is probably not a soaring pilot worthy of the name who, were he arbitrarily limited to a single instrument, would not toss out everything but his favorite Memphis, Badin or Crossfell. The story of the instrument itself has never been told, so far as we know. Until the day it is, we offer these spare details.

One ancestor of the modern variometer was the statoscope, a device developed by balloonists to record the fact, although not the rate, of ascent and descent. Vertical as well as horizontal motion in the atmosphere was a concern of balloon pilots from a very early date and the creation of an instrument to record rise and fall was a natural step. Furthermore, balloonists seem to have been aware of the updrafts associated with cumulus clouds a long while before sailplane pilots began taking advantage of them. It seems reasonable to assume that, had a few experienced balloonists been drawn into gliding at an early date, the history of thermal soaring might have been altered significantly.

Soaring nonetheless owes ballooning a debt on account of the variometer that ultimately evolved from the statoscope. Alexander Lippisch, whose extraordinary career seems to have touched every aspect of flying, acquired one of these, an Atmos, to use in flight tests of Dornier airplanes. That was in 1918. A decade later, when Kronfeld was busily engaged exploring the underside of cumulus clouds in search of lift, Lippisch suggested a variometer to him. Kronfeld promptly obtained an Atmos from Paris and secreted it in his *Wien*. There was some curiosity about the vacuum flask that accompanied the instrument, but the curious were assured that it simply contained coffee.

The same year Kronfeld made the first soaring flights using a variometer, a book entitled *The Baghdad Air Mail* was published in England. Sir Roderic Hill, the author, describes in the book the difficulties he and other pioneer air-mail pilots had in getting their sluggish Vickers *Vernons* to climb in the thin, hot air of the desert, especially when fully loaded. As a matter of necessity the *Vernon* pilots began making use of *dunts*—their name for thermals.

Methods of detecting *dunts* varied, even as they do today. One pilot did nothing more than locate a soaring kite and join him in his thermal. Another ingenious fellow invented a dunt indicator. "It was extremely simple," Sir Roderic wrote, "consisting of an empty two-gallon petrol tin fixed behind the pilot's instrument board. The cap was sealed on, but through it was drilled a tiny hole. The tin was connected by a small pipe to one side of a pressure gauge visible to the pilot. The other side of the pressure gauge was open to the air in the pilot's cockpit."

Despite the actual use of a variometer, and despite the published account of how to construct one, the secret weapon continued to remain a secret for some time to come. When, in 1930, Wolf Hirth made his famous cross-country flight from Elmira using blue-sky thermals it was primarily with the help of soaring birds. In later years Hirth carried natural soaring techniques to their logical conclusion by detecting thermals by means of the sensations in his ears. It seems likely that soaring birds use precisely this technique, probably in conjunction with one or two others, in locating lift. At any rate the bird's ear drum is constructed so as to be more sensitive to up-currents, while in man just the opposite is the case. As with many of his other shortcomings, however, man can compensate with his brain and his hands.

## Vignettes from The Perilous and Poignant Past (No. 119)

THE TIME WAS early in World War II; the place, the Royal Aircraft Establishment at Farnborough, England. The protagonist is Squadron Leader Dougie Davie, the writer, Lawrence Wright:

"Among other devices, he tried out an automatic pilot fitted in a Hotspur, to be used on tow. It had worked well, and was being demonstrated to a load of senior officers, when the tug throttled back in cloud, and the glider overtook it. The slack rope lassoed the glider's nose, then tightened and peeled the fuselage like a banana. The Hotspur was the older type with a removable lid, and this too the rope removed, leaving the passengers as in an open boat. That at least made their exit easier, and all but Dougie baled out. He then decided that the glider was just controllable, and landed back at Farnborough, to await the return and comments of the passengers."

—*The Wooden Sword*

## Dynamic Soaring

AS LONG AGO as 1883, in what was certainly one of the most inspired comments ever made on the subject, Lord Rayleigh stated that soaring flight required either a wind that was not horizontal, or one that was not of uniform velocity. Today, the better part of a century later, we seem to have no knoweldge that could be used to argue against this brilliant hypothesis.

WINDS NOT HORIZONTAL — slope winds, thermal upcurrents, convergence zones and evening valley circulation chief among them — are by far the more easily exploited of the two types and have been extensively explored and analyzed by glider pilots since Rayleigh's day. WINDS NOT OF UNIFORM VELOCITY relate to the more recondite matter of dynamic soaring and have proven to be considerably less accessible to man and his machines than those of the non-horizontal variety. Nevertheless dynamic soaring has long been one of the more romantic concerns of gliding experimenters. In the earlier days of the sport, when many theories had yet to be tested, and before the ability of the albatross was as fully appreciated as it is today, the technique of dynamic soaring occupied many an astute theoretician and many noteworthy contributions to the art were made.

The Germans, whose early contributions to gliding were so far in advance of other nations, did the majority of the pioneering work and made the greatest progress in dynamic soaring. Wolfgang Klemperer, who we have met elsewhere in this work, had a long-time concern with both the theory and practice of dynamic flight. It was his contention that rhythmic oscillation of the elevator, made while flying through vertically pulsating air, could yield "an optimum power gain a little in excess of that natural gain which would be derived from inertia alone"—providing the pilot could anticipate the incipient gusts and react appropriately to them!

Klemperer's third glider, the Aachen *Ente* of 1922, was built specifically to experiment with gust flying. It was a canard type, that is with the horizontal tail forward of the wing. This configuration was adopted in the hope that frontal gusts, acting on the forward surface and momentarily increasing the angle of attack of the wing, would tend automatically to utilize variations in the relative wind. The tail-first design was considerably less satisfactory in practice than in theory, however, and moveover suffered from longitudinal instability.

Klemperer's canard configuration was only one of a number of methods used to try to trap the elusive gust gradient. The method which seemed to have the most in its favor, and the one most commonly employed, was to mount the wing so that it pivoted about its longitudinal axis on a line near the center of pressure. The Darmstadt *Geheimrat,* also of 1922, featured such a system. In flight the elevator of the *Geheimrat* was to be left locked in position and the longitudinal control, as well as response to favorable gusts, managed by manipulation of the wing. Only in the event of the pilot finding himself in an attitude from which he could not recover by use of the wing alone would the elevator be brought into play.

The wing-controlled gliders, although probably superior to other variants, presented structural problems that were not easily mastered. The forward tail of the *Ente* was one way around the problem. Another was the aileron linkage used on a monoplane glider designed by Finsterwalder and Von Lossl and built by the Bavarian Aero Club in 1921. In this ship changes in the angle of attack of the wing were effected by rotating both ailerons in the same direction, while lateral control was maintained in the usual manner, by aileron rotation in opposite directions.

For about a decade prior to the time the *Ente* and *Geheimrat* were built two very remarkable men, one a German, the other French, had been devoting considerable attention to the matter of dynamic soaring. Both of them produced imaginative soaring machines and one some remarkable results. Like their precise contemporary, Weiss, they have been largely ignored by their posterity, possibly because they were so far ahead of their time that we have not yet caught up with them.

It seems quite probable that Dr. Magnan, the Frenchman, was familiar with the ideas of Lord Rayleigh concerning the nature of the winds necessary for soaring flight and also conversant with the work of his own countryman, Pierre Idrac, who investigated the mechanics of the soaring flight of vultures and of the albatross in Africa at about the turn of the century. In 1914 Magnan produced two gliders, one patterned after the vulture, the other after the albatross. The first of these two gliders even featured tip slots, six to a panel; the second had an aspect ratio of 15. Both had cantilevered wings, streamlined fuselages, conventional tail surfaces and were, withal, very modern looking.

As proved the case with his German counterpart, Harth, Magnan's work was interrupted by the Great War. But in 1921 he produced his type M-2. Like the pre-war designs, this was a cantilever monoplane. Perhaps its most outstanding feature was the method Magnan devised to utilize horizontal gusts. The wing halves were, in effect, slid over a pair of rectangular box-beam spars to which they were attached by sets of springs that permitted each panel to respond to changes in the relative wind and to *adapt itself* to atmospheric variations. The pilot's seat of the M-2 was so included in the elevator linkage that a forward stick movement not only depressed the control surface, but also moved the pilot forward in the cockpit as well!

Like so much of the rest of his work, Dr. Magnan's approach to testing the M-2 was preeminently practical. The glider was suspended on a wire hung between two poles in a manner that kept it tethered and facing the wind. Horizontal and vertical gusts in the immediate vicinity of the glider were monitored by dynamometers and the readings, presumably, compared to the recorded weight of the glider from moment to moment. Some manner of flight tests were made, but these appear to have been inconclusive.

* * *

FREDERICK HARTH, if we are to judge by the results he obtained in the art of dynamic soaring, was not only several strides ahead of Magnan, but was one of the most original and pertinacious of all aviation pioneers. Harth was a Bavarian, a native of Bamberg, who achieved more significant results, it seems, than anyone else who has thus far attempted dynamic soaring. He was an architect who appears to have been attracted to flying primarily on account of the mechanical problems it presented. He began his career in aviation in 1910, at the age of 44, on the gentle slopes of the Heidelstein in the Rhön Mountains near his home. Assisting him in his experiments was a younger man who was to achieve a certain measure of success in the world of aviation in the years to come. His name was Willi Messerschmidtt.

Harth and Messerschmidtt were active until the beginning of the first World War, did some work during the war and, like Magnan, returned to their pursuits when the slaughter ended. Although toward the end of his career Harth built a glider with an enclosed fuselage, the majority of his machines were of the primary type, with open trusswork between the wing and tail surfaces. It seems fair to guess that it was Harth who originated the wing pivoting arrangement used by others later. Control of the wing was effected by two sizeable levers through which gust loads were transmitted to the pilot and by means of which the pilot altered the angle of incidence of the wing as he saw fit. Not only could the required incidence changes be made by moving both levers in the same direction simultaneously, but the glider could be turned by using the levers in opposition.

As early as January of 1914, and again in 1916, Harth made successful flights in gliders of his own design, in one instance staying in the air for 3½ minutes! In 1920 he made a number of

Wolf Hirth at the controls of one of Frederic Harth's gliders of the sort that established a world duration record in 1921.

flights of up to 6 minutes duration over a slope with an incline of only 2 to 3 degrees, hardly enough to furnish a slope wind adequate even to keep the ultra-light machines of Harth airborne. In September of the following year—Harth's 55th!—he was back on the Heidlestein. At 8:30 on the morning of the 13th of that month he flew for 21 minutes and 30 seconds. During this flight, which constituted a world record for duration, he attained an altitude of nearly 600 feet above his take-off point and ranged as far as a mile from the spot he began, and terminated, his flight.

The German aviation magazine *Flugsport* called attention to the fact that Harth's flight had been made over a plain, a fact that would eliminate the hypothesis that the pilot had used slope winds for his feat. There has seemed to be very little desire to give Harth credit for dynamic soaring in this instance. It is, of course, quite possible that he contributed with his manipulations only a fraction of the energy necessary for such flight and got the remainder from some then-unrecognized form of lift in the area. Be that as it may, Harth demonstrated dynamic soaring on this and other occasions in a most dramatic way: he launched himself completely independently by waiting on an upslope, facing the wind, and using an opportune gust to literally hike himself into the air by his bootstraps.

Harth, as may reasonably be expected, had sacrificed much to the lightness of his gliders. His Heidelstein machine had just over 160 sq.ft. of wing area (the equivalent of the Schweizer 1-26 and the *Vampyr*) and weighed in at just a bit over 100 lbs. The resulting fragility, coupled with the extraordinary exertions that must have been necessary by the pilot, were a potentially dangerous combination that resulted, in 1921, in a serious crash. Harth was badly hurt, particularly about the head, and although he recovered adequately to resume flying he never again matched his achievements of earlier years.

Harth's retirement from activity at just the moment when Klemperer, Martens, Hentzen and the other practitioners of slope soaring were having such spectacular successes on the Wasserkuppe, and with a form of gliding which ultimately demanded a great deal less from the pilot, put his efforts into eclipse in somewhat the same manner that gliding itself had suffered when the infernal combustion engine helped turn the attention of the world from the glories of motorless flight to that cruder adaptation of the airplane that was inaugurated on December 17th, 1903. Taken all in all, Frederic Harth seems to have been one of those individuals who, in his accomplishments, not only outstripped his contemporaries, but the just desserts such accomplishments merit.

* * *

NO REVIEW OF DYNAMIC SOARING would be complete without reference to a still earlier experimenter, also a Bavarian, Ing. Wolfmuller of Munich. In 1909, a year of inestimable consequence for aviation, Wolfmuller built a glider which, it is not difficult to believe, inspired both Magnan and Harth in somewhat the same manner as Harth's successes seem to have inspired Klemperer and the builders of the *Geheimrat*. Like the machines of Magnan, it was a streamlined monoplane with a cantilever wing. It was evidently meant to be adaptable to either of Lord Rayleigh's winds, but it is to those not of uniform velocity to which we turn our interest.

The wing of the Wolfmuller machine, which had a span of some 32 feet, was patterned after that of a soaring bird, having the six slots per panel common to the vulture. The wing seems to have been rotated at the leading edge, not near the center of pressure as with the Magnan and Harth gliders. This was unquestionably a serious weakness. The fuselage was squat and birdlike. The pointed nose was covered with a transparent material, possibly mica, which gives rise to the suspicion that the pilot was to have assumed a prone position during flight. The tail was a flat, splayed V similar to that of birds such as the pigeon. The controls were completely enclosed in the fuselage, a very unusual refinement for the day.

It is hardly surprising that a machine so far ahead of its time and incorporating so many radical innovations was not successfully flown. Ing. Wolfmuller, however, did fly some heavier-than-air dynamic soaring craft and, providing the Chinese or the Tibetans or the Aztecs or the Arabs or some other heathens didn't beat him to it, may have been the first man in history to do so.

It is not improbable to assume that Wolfmuller, who was, incidentally, a pupil of Lilienthal, realized that dynamic soaring could be achieved by one of three methods. Outwardly the simplest of these, yet really the most refined, is to devise an aerodynamic form that modifies itself constantly in order to utilize gradient energy. The second is to commute between two layers of the wind, alternately storing and expending energy in the passages back and forth, as the wandering albatross does. The third is to build a flying machine of such dimensions that it effectively spans two layers of the atmosphere and utilizes the velocity gradient between them in much the same fashion that a sailboat, with its keel in the water and its sail in the air, works between two elements. This is what Ing. Wolfmuller did.

Although on first hearing this idea sounds a bit outlandish it is really so simple that anyone can do it with material costing only a dollar or two. The magic ingredients are two kites and some string or wire. Provided that there is a sufficient gradient between two layers of wind, or wind from two directions, the kites can be made to sail off as a set simply by tethering them to opposite ends of a suitable length of line. Once released they will rise through the gradient until their weight-plus-drag is equal to the force generated by the stratum in which they operate, much as a balloon finds its point of stability in the atmosphere. Such kites, by properly rigging them, can be made to sail across the wind.

The idea of tethering two gliders together, nose to nose, and flying them in a similar manner, has occurred to a number of people. The problem of an adequate gradient would seem to have been solved by the discovery of the jet stream and someone may yet manage a cross-continental soaring flight by this intriguing means, provided a few minor problems can be solved.

* * *

THE AUTHOR, who alternately finds himself either a century ahead of the times, or a century behind, has listed among his Future Projects Number 719(W), or GRANDIOSE SCHEME FOR THE CASUAL CIRCUMNAVIGATION OF THE GREAT TERRESTIAL SPHERE WITHOUT MECHANICAL MEANS AND AVOIDING CUSTOMS—an obvious extrapolation of the work of Wolfmuller. However in this hot-paced age, when speed and expediency are valued above all other qualities, 719(W) seems doomed to failure; so the author, to save himself undue frustration, shifts the whole matter into fantasy and turns the clock back . . .

It is *fin de siecle,* the tail end of the age that brought the world the steam engine, the electric light, the engine-powered dirigible, wireless and railroads that span continents. The protagonists in our fantasy—Jules Verne, Tom Swift and Horatio Algerstein—are an amalgam of the most fortuitous talents of the age and a trinity whose individual contributions of imagination, implementation and impertinence culminate in an undertaking of such enormity, one so daring, yet devoid of real risk, one so presumptuous, yet plausible, that it strikes the common and uncommon mind alike with its stunning, galvanic force.

From the English industrial heartland come powerful windlasses and miles of fine steel cable; from the Zeppelin factories on the Continent, great girders and trusses; from Japan immense bolts of buff silk; from America the latest in lighting equipment.

The inventors, at work in huge sheds on the Atlantic seacoast, labor through the winter in shrouded secrecy. In the first warm days of spring mighty sections of framework are transported to a near-by beach where they are bolted together. As the silk covering is applied the shapes of two incredibly large airfoils, each with a chord of several hundred feet and a span of half a mile, emerge.

By autumn the aerial giant is complete and preparations for launching are made. The first of the two airfoils is kited to an altitude of several thousand feet using ponderous concrete blocks as anchors. Next the lower airfoil, all properly rigged, is made ready. As the day designated for the launching arrives great crowds gather to watch those who are to make the trip mount the motorized bosun's chair that climbs, time and again, the slender wire that disappears, through occasional puffs of cloud, in the direction of the wing waiting high overhead. Finally the last preparations are made. A green flare, the signal to begin, arcs down through the sky. Stout men, on command, raise their axes and with concerted cuts sever the hausers that hold the great engine tied to Earth . . .

Effortlessly the unfettered machine slips into the air, falters just a moment, then takes its heading down the wind. Miles above the earth, isolate in the spacious glass cabin at the center of the upper wing, the passengers watch the coast recede and feel themselves borne ever higher on the buoyant breezes. From the control room, with its banks of switches and levers, its rows of dimly lit dials, its compasses and charts, go the commands that cause the windlasses to churn that steer the behemoth along the vastest ocean of the world.

As daylight fades the red and blue navigation lights flicker across the gray expanses of fabric. The stars tremble into existence, and on the wings meander through the oceanic twilight. Snug within their cabins, hearts rounded with hope, the aerial adventurers converse on irrational numbers and imcommensurable quantities and, providing they get up early enough in the morning, imagine three impossible things before breakfast.